COMPARTMENT FIREFIGHTING SERIES: VOLUME 2

# Reading Fire

## A complete scene assessment guide
## for firefighters and practitioners at all levels

The trusted voice of fire & emergency since 1908

Pavilion

**Benjamin Walker** BA(Hons) MIFireE (Godiva Award)

with **Shan Raffel** AFSM EngTech CFIFireE

# Reading Fire

A complete scene assessment guide for firefighters and practitioners at all levels

**Published by:**
Pavilion Publishing and Media Ltd
Rayford House
School Road
Hove
East Sussex
BN3 5HX
Tel: 01273 434 943
Fax: 01273 227 308
Email: info@pavpub.com

Ben Walker's royalties will be donated to the International Fire & Rescue Association

Published 2017

A catalogue record for this book is available from the British Library.

ISBN: 978-1-911028-73-4

*Pavilion is the leading training and development provider and publisher in the health, social care and allied fields, providing a range of innovative training solutions underpinned by sound research and professional values. We aim to put our customers first, through excellent customer service and value.*

**Authors:** Benjamin Walker, with Shan Raffel
**Production editor:** Mike Benge, Pavilion Publishing and Media Ltd
**Cover design:** Tony Pitt, Pavilion Publishing and Media Ltd
**Page layout and typesetting:** Emma Dawe, Pavilion Publishing and Media Ltd
**Printing:** CMP Digital Print Solutions

# Contents

# About the authors

**Benjamin Walker** started his career in the Metropolitan Tyne & Wear Fire Brigade, working and commanding some of Europe's busiest fire stations. Following a spell at a small rural fire department, he moved to study in the United States, obtaining several fire service certifications and studying FEMA's Emergency Management qualifications.

Returning to the UK to train the London Fire Brigade, he was recognised by the Institution of Fire Engineers, winning the Godiva Award and taking a place upon a branch board to strengthen the future of the fire services through the Young Professional's Network.

In demand as a presenter and instructor, he has taught on multiple occasions at the world's largest conference, FDIC in Indianapolis, and remains determined in his pursuit of reducing firefighter line of duty deaths worldwide.

Ben currently teaches any fire department that wants to improve their compartment firefighting abilities and is contactable through his website www.benwalkerfirefighter.com. He performs outreach work with the International Fire & Rescue Association (www.ifra.co.uk) worldwide.

**Shan Raffel** has served as a career firefighter in Brisbane, Australia, since 1983. After the death of two colleagues in 1994, and the serious injury of two others in 1996, he submitted a proposal for an intensive international study of compartment fire behaviour training (CFBT). This was successful and in 1997 he was sent to the UK and Sweden for six weeks to study the most advanced teaching methods and training facilities. On his return he developed the first nationally recognised training program in Australia and has since assisted numerous fire services in Australia and internationally with the development of their training facilities and teaching materials.

In 2009 he was awarded a 'Churchill Fellowship' to research 'Planning Preparation and Response to Emergencies in Tunnels', which led to intensive study over a period of 10 weeks in the USA with the FDNY, Canada, Germany, Austria, Sweden, Denmark, Norway and Switzerland. He used this knowledge to develop the construction and operational phase emergency response plans for the three largest road tunnels in Australia.

He has presented at numerous international conferences, contributes regularly to fire journals and co-authored *3D Fire Fighting*, which was published in 2005 by Fire Protection Publications (Oklahoma State University).

# Foreword

## Neil Gibbins, QFSM FIFireE President of the Institution of Fire Engineers 2014/15.

I first met Ben when he attended the IFE AGM to collect his Godiva Award for achieving the highest marks in an IFE examination. I was immediately struck by his energy and passion, which when added to his knowledge (clearly demonstrated by his outstanding exam marks) creates a very powerful persona. I suspected that we might meet again, and here we are looking at Ben's second book, which he has put together with Shan Raffel. I am delighted to provide a few words for the front of this book, the natural follow up to the first volume, *Fire Dynamics for Firefighters*. This is so relevant to many operational firefighters today, to help them do their job safely and effectively.

In my formative firefighting years we would often hear a mantra credited to Massey Shaw, pointing out (I paraphrase poorly) that firefighters need to be able to get inside a burning building, access the fire and use the equipment they have with them to deal with it. In a properly organised fire service, the decision to commit firefighters to the inside of a building on fire is a decision that is only made after the risk has been assessed. To carry out that assessment, the assessor must be equipped with the relevant knowledge to make the defensive/offensive call. My peers were taught by firefighters who had served in the war years. They might not have been involved in the effects of war, but they worked very long hours and dealt with hundreds of jobs in their careers. They drilled (another old fashioned term) into me what I believed were 'the basics' of firefighting, signs and actions that became normal, second nature. It might sound like firefighting by numbers, indeed it was for training, but it worked, and key signals became embedded so they became almost instinctive. Time moves on, Massey Shaw still holds good, but what has changed?

From the late 50s through to the early 2000s, wholetime promotion required successful completion of a knowledge test. Written exams brought focus to studies; manuals of firemanship were well thumbed and tested. The introduction of the integrated personal development system (IPDS) in 2003, however, saw the end of statutory exams. Thankfully, many UK FRS are utilising some IFE exams, but this isn't the case everywhere. In my first year in the job, my station turned out over 2,000 times. Not a lot, some might say, but today the number for that station is under 500. Spread between four watches, not three. The point I make is that firefighters in the UK today have less opportunity to deploy their skills, and in many instances have no formal tests of underpinning knowledge or structure for learning. Many, if not most, of the UK officers turning out in charge of fire engines, making decisions to commit firefighters into burning buildings, will, in my opinion, really value Ben and Shan's work. We should celebrate the success of fire prevention and every action that has led to the reduction in fires and deaths, but recognise that we are now operating in a new paradigm.

So how does this book (indeed this whole series) help? Ben and Shan translate scientific principles into a form that is easily related to their practical application. They have gathered together the learning about interpreting fires in buildings in a 'modern' context and committed words to paper in 'modern' style. I like reading it. It's not full of jargon, but I think firefighters (especially in the UK and USA) will relate to it and recognise their language. It is broken down into manageable and readable chunks. Ben and Shan tell us what they are going to tell us, do the explanation, and then summarise. This makes the points you need to remember really clear and more likely to be recalled when needed. In the middle of the night, in the rain, with everyone looking to you to make the call. Safely.

I thoroughly recommend this book to all students of fire, whether studying to prepare for a firefighting role, an incident command role or indeed any role where the understanding of fire behaviour might lead to better decision making. You will find the words easy to digest and the diagrams complement the words perfectly. Well done guys! I look forward to the next one. And well done to you for deciding to read it.

# Acknowledgements

Books 2 and 3 of the Compartment Firefighting Series have seen so many international colleagues come together to offer advice, support and information that it would take pages to mention everyone. So, with apologies to anyone unintentionally missed, please see the list below.

A special mention must go to my co-author and inspiration Shan Raffel for the hours of countless dedication, counsel and motivation, and to Mike Benge, our editor, friend and the man who makes legible sense from my gibberish and ramblings. Bill Gough and Anita Pickerden have been pillars of support and pioneers in driving the fire service forward, as have Dr Paul Grimwood, Ed Hartin and John McDonough. Martin Arrowsmith has truly been an unsung hero of the fire service for many years and it is a privilege for me to recognise his contribution here. I'd also like to thank the Institution of Fire Engineers and CEO Neil Gibbins for their ceaseless efforts at driving forward the professional standards of the industry. And Bobby Halton – simply inspirational.

In no particular order:

The team at KTF Burns – Andrew and Joe Starnes; the team at HydroVent – Kevin, Ryan and Nick; the team at FireDex – Tony Moore, Allen Rom and Bill Burke; the team at FDIC PennWell  - Bobby, Diane, Ginger, Erich and Mark; Priscilla Morris, for assisting me adapt the written word to the spoken.

Our European friends: Szymon Kokot Gora, Pablo-Boj Garcia, Professor Stefan Svensson, Lars Axelsson, CFBT Roy, Stephane Morizot, Dietmar Kuhn, Juan Carlos Campana, Siemco Baaj, Karel Lambert, Arturo Arnalich, Idan Braun, Tizano Pojer, George Bogkias, John Chubb, Michael Reick, Lasse Nelson, Gearoid Blake and Christophe Albert.

From North America: Bruce Varner, Peter McBride, Ian Bolton, Paul Enhelder, Alan and Nick Brunacini, Dave Casey, Christopher Naum, Brad Davidson, Jerry Tracy, Jack Murphy, Dennis Rubin, Commissioner Jose Santiago (Chicago FD), Ric Jorge, Bob Carpenter, Ken Himel, OJ, Commissioner Adam Thiel (Philadelphia FD) Commissioner Daniel Nigro (FDNY) Mike Gagliano, James Strohecker, Ray McCormack, Eddie Buchanan, Brian Kazmazairk, Pete Lamb, John Dixon, Christopher Baker and Stephen Kerber (ULFSRI).

From South America: Walter Pizzaro, Rafael Antonio, Ricardo Hasche, Mathias Gonzalez, Alfredo Chavez, Elvio Rafael Schindele and Saul Tello Montenegro.

From Australasia: Jae Yang Yang (Jeff!), Greg Henry, Andrew Sharrad and Blaine Clancy.

From the UK Fire Services: Dave Payton, Iain Evans and the team at WMFS BA, CFO Phil Loach (West Midlands FS), CFO Peter O Reilly (Greater Manchester FRS), CFO Dan Stephens (Merseyside FRS), Commissioner Danielle Cotton (London Fire Brigade), Asst Commissioner Dominic Evans (LFB), CFO Chris Blacksell (Humberside FRS), CFO Becky Bryant (Staffordshire FRS), DCFO Rob Barber (Staffs), Stephen Burns, Garry Teasdale, David Curran, Sean McKee, Laura Lawrence, Phil Wright, Pete Ahmed and Vince O' Neill. James Rossano Bull, Stephen Duffy, Darren Masini, Kevin Longshaw, Nick Searle, Michael Broadley, Andy Hallworth, Stephen Harrison, Neil Flynn, Philip Dean, John Percy, Jim Dave, Matt Swan, Dave Wilson, Steve Pritchard, Allan Holloway, Glenn Miller, Michael Lewis, Tonia Jarret and Tyrone Richards.

From the UK, the Walker family, Insley family, Rob Wakelin, Matt Aitken, Jack Lovett, Jim McCabe, David Kay OBE and all at IFRA, Lindsay Morris, Nick Jeffs, Gavin Clapp, Andrew Lynch, Ellie Thackway and Paul Basson.

For all the unsung heroes trying to drive progress

# Introduction

Thanks for joining me once more for this second volume of the Compartment Firefighting Series. In this volume we'll be taking a look at how we can effectively use the knowledge acquired in the first book, *Fire Dynamics for Firefighters*, and apply it to the emergency incidents which we attend swiftly and safely.

The ability to read a fire, to determine what stage it's at and how various factors might affect its growth is an essential skill for all firefighters. Armed with this information, the firefighter can make tactical decisions based, for example, on the type of building in which the fire is present, environmental conditions that might have a bearing on the fire or the specific conditions in the compartment on fire at any given time. To help us with this, we have the 'BE-SAHF' model of 'size up' – a simple acronym that can quickly guide our investigations to highlight all the important areas that need our consideration before we decide what actions to take. The model looks at the following areas:

- **B** – building
- **E** – environment

- **S** – smoke
- **A** – air
- **H** – heat
- **F** – flame

It is these areas that guide the structure of this book. We will look at each of them in turn, exploring the salient points and trying to understand the full situation we are presented with when we arrive at the scene of a fire.

The next volume in this series, *Volume 3: Fighting Fire*, will then look at the tactics that can be used depending on what information you can gain from using the BE-SAHF model to assess a fire.

With this volume and the next, I have the great privilege of being assisted, guided, motivated and often counselled by my great friend and co-author Shan Raffel of the Queensland, Australia Fire & Emergency Services. As the architect of the BE-SAHF model, this book wouldn't have been possible without his pioneering work.

If you enjoy this book, you will definitely enjoy attending his many lectures and workshops and applying them on the fireground. As an added bonus, Shan has the ultimate 'reading fire' book on the way, which builds, expands and further explains in detail the concepts that we take a more basic look at this book.

Once again, I am standing on the shoulders of giants, merely providing an access point to the work of those much more skilled and educated than myself who have generously assisted with their expertise and knowledge in individual sections.

**This book series is dedicated to the enduring memories of Firefighter Paul Barrow and Firefighter Billy Vinton of the Tyne & Wear Metropolitan Fire Brigade.**

# Chapter 1:
# Revising Volume 1 –
# The guiding principles

In Volume 1 of this series we covered the stages of development that a fire moves through and we observed a basic graph detailing this when a fire has sufficient air to sustain its development – a 'fuel-controlled' fire profile.

## Figure 1.1: The development of a fire

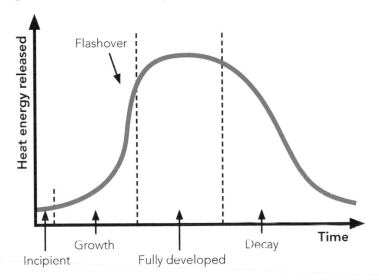

We also observed how modern materials, as fire loading, can quickly use up available air to a fire and how the rate and stage of fire development is limited by the amount of this air. This is known as a 'ventilation-controlled' fire profile. As Figure 1.2 shows, however, the actions of firefighters 'opening up', ventilating, or even just by their actions in trying to locate a fire, such as opening doors while moving through buildings, can all affect the development of a fire and cause the fire to begin developing again.

## Figure 1.2: Unwanted ventilation

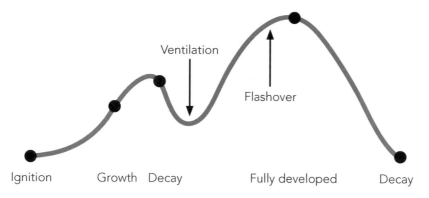

Fire presents extreme dangers and risks and many firefighters have been caught out by what we term 'rapid fire developments', often caused by this sudden ventilation of a previously ventilation-controlled fire. So, let's re-cover what we covered in Volume 1 about these phenomena.

You will recall that we covered the three rapid fire developments:

■ Flashover

■ Backdraft

■ Fire Gas Ignition

Feel free to consult your copy of Volume 1 to revise these, but let's now take a look at the signs and symptoms of each.

**Flashover:** Approaching flashover can be indicated by a number of factors, some of these include, but aren't limited to:

■ a rapid increase in temperature

■ the lowering of the neutral plane (smoke layer)

■ flames in the gas layer/smoke on fire (rollover)

■ pyrolysis of all combustible surfaces and pyrolysis at floor level

■ fire gas turbulence.

**Backdraft:** There are a range of indicators that we are approaching a backdraft situation, including:

- A low or 'bouncing' neutral plane.

- Gases exiting from gaps under pressure.

- Exiting gases igniting (diluting into the flammable range at an auto-ignition temperature).

- 'Pulsing/breathing gases'.

- Inrush of air when an opening is created.

- Turbulent fire gases exiting, altering in pace, colour and composition.

- 'The wedge' created at an opening between exiting gas and inrushing air.

- Blackened windows.

**Fire Gas Ignition:** FGI requires slightly more consideration as its signs and symptoms are less obvious or even unexpected, and this has caught many firefighters out. Indicators include:

- an accumulation of fire gases in a compartment known to be remote from the fire's origin

- indications of heat from floors, walls, ceilings in rooms with no fire

- pyrolysis of any surface, especially those which are on or are near compartment boundaries.

However, tactically, the approaches and techniques we use will also be governed by the potential for these rapid fire developments and how we can tackle them, maximising firefighter safety while achieving our goals. Fortunately, we can anticipate (although we can never assume) that some of these developments are more likely in certain situations than others. We will explore these in the following chapters.

# The PVT principles

Some final revision involves the gas laws, or, as we defined them in Volume 1, the firefighter's PVT (pressure/volume/temperature) principles, as related to fire gas/smoke.

The principle states that increasing temperatures will increase the volume of a gas, and that this expansion will continue until a 'container' (such as a closed room's walls, floor and ceilings) is found. At this point the gas cannot expand much further as it is restricted by the size of the container, and so the volume of fire gas is held constant. If this is the case, and the temperature continues to increase, then the pressure of the gas will also increase – thus we may see highly pressurised gases trying to escape from any miniscule gaps it can find.

We also know that fire gases will move from areas of higher pressure to those of lower pressure (like letting helium gas out of a balloon as it moves to atmosphere). We can use this knowledge to plan when we create openings which fire gases are going to flow to. Simply opening and closing doors can be a form of 'tactical ventilation' and flowpath management.

To conclude, we need to remember that each flowpath of air has two aspects – an inlet flowpath heading towards a fire, and an outlet flowpath heading away from a fire. Depending on the opening, these can be 'unidirectional', with separate openings for each flowpath – one in, one out – or they can be 'bidirectional', where one opening is acting as both an inlet opening and exhaust opening. In these cases we will see fire gas exiting and air entering from the same opening, usually with a clearly defined smoke layer (or neutral plane) between where these different pressures meet (see figures 1.3 and 1.4).

## Figure 1.3 : A unidirectional flowpath

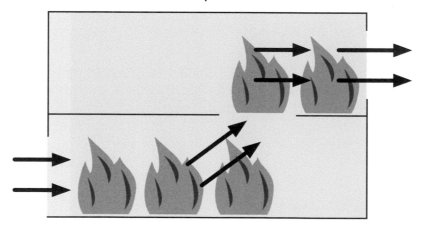

## Figure 1.4: A bidirectional flowpath

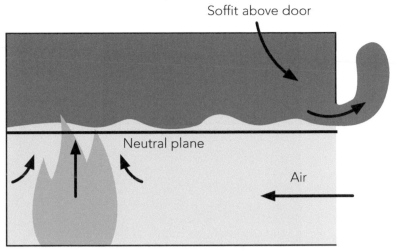

So, wrapping up some brief revision, we should all be back on the page with our terminology, signs and symptoms, gas laws and fire behaviour basics. These need to be deeply embedded in our minds so we can anticipate, recognise and act on this information in order to stay safe and achieve our goal – putting fires out!

# Chapter 2: Introducing the 'size up' and BE-SAHF

Size ups, or making scene assessments, are as old as the fire service itself. I have no doubt that as ancient Rome burned and Emperor Nero broke out a tune on his violin, some centurion or other, put in charge of this situation, was trying to work out what was happening, what could viably be saved (strategy), what could viably be done with the resources (tactics), and how it could be done (task/operations). I'm sure we've all been in situations where we've had to make an assessment of a similar kind.

The issues that have faced the fire service in making assessments have changed in recent years as we fill our buildings with contents that contain much more energy and have much higher potential heat release rates than 30 years ago, influencing the speed of a fire's spread and its movement through the stages of development. Furthermore, changes in constructional methods and fixed installations have added more complexity to how a building will or can perform in a fire situation, to both the advantage and disadvantage of firefighters.

However, we can still use the knowledge that we acquired in Volume 1 to excellent effect by understanding and analysing the dynamics of a fire to answer the following questions with regard to the fire behaviour:

- What is happening now?
- What are the risks of the current situation?
- What could happen if this continues? (Where is the fire and smoke going if we don't intervene?)
- What will/could happen if we make an intervention or take action? (How can we use ventilation and extinguishing tactics in synergy to produce the best outcome in each situation?)

Most fire departments will have methods of calculating risk, formulating plans and making decisions. However, the information we gather during a size up depends on our knowledge of fire dynamics and our ability to recognise situations and base decisions upon this, known as 'recognition primed decision making'.

This knowledge and these skills allow us to gather the most comprehensive information we can and plan effectively with contingencies as required.

# Being safe

The concept of a 'model' of scene assessment looking specifically at the features of fire behaviour was developed by Shan Raffel and detailed in his work with Paul Grimwood, Ed Hartin and John McDonough, the pivotal *3D Firefighting* (2005)[1]. The model that was initially proposed involved the assessment of four key areas of a fire in order to read its behaviour: smoke, air, heat and flame, giving the model its name – 'SAHF'.

Naturally, over the last 12 years this model has developed as Shan, Ed, Paul, John and others across the world have taken this foundation and added to and adapted it. Sadly, however, firefighters continue to die in the line of duty when the knowledge we have gained, knowledge explored in Volume 1 of this series, and its application in an effective size up could and should have changed these tragic outcomes.

# So where are we now?

The model has evolved from SAHF (smoke, air, heat and flame) to BE-SAHF, with Chief Ed Hartin in the USA adding **B**uilding factors and Peter McBride in Canada suggesting **E**nvironmental factors as part of the context in which fire behaviour indicators are read. This model has now incorporated these additions as critical factors to be evaluated as part of any size up as they undoubtedly can have a huge impact on any fire and our tactics need to reflect this accordingly. The current BE-SAHF model of assessment looks like this:

---

1    Highly recommended, even compulsory, as further, in-depth reading to accompany this book. More articles on this and other subjects can be found at www.3dfirefighting.com/index.php/authors/shan-raffel.

## The BE-SAHF size up

B    Building Factors

E    Environmental Factors

### The Context
Building: Ed Hartin 2005
Environmental Factors: Peter McBride 2014

S    Smoke Indicators

A    Air

H    Heat Indicators

F    Flame indicators

### Fire Behaviour Indicators
Shan Raffel 1999

In this volume we are going to take a look at each of these BE-SAHF concepts in turn and use what we know from Volume 1 in order to 'read the fire', again, working out what is happening, what is likely to happen without our actions, what our actions or interventions could make happen, and then take these into consideration when making our plan of attack, using the skills, techniques and tools available to us.

We must remember that, as with any emergency situation, these categories are not exclusive or separate to each other; they all overlap, synergise and work together to give clues as to what is happening with a fire – most importantly, its location or origin. It is almost certain that in the initial chaos of arriving at an emergency incident we won't be able to conduct a comprehensive analysis of every factor, but with a solid understanding of the background and through practice and experience, BE-SAHF is a quick and effective reference guide for fire size up and tactical selection.

We will not examine each concept individually on the fireground since they all interlink, but we will consider each in a wider context to gain a complete perspective before we implement our plans. By examining the background in a little more depth here, we can enhance our capacity to interpret and understand on the fireground.

# Chapter 3: Reading fire step 1 – building and construction

Well, here we are underway and starting to think about how we can fight fires, and this section is arguably the foundation stone upon which we can build our knowledge to do it effectively.

Building and construction used to be a fundamental aspect of firefighter training and it is important to know how buildings are put together, and how they can fall apart. Elements of constructions such as beams, columns, floors and walls can all react differently in fires and affect the stage of development as well as the potential for rapid fire developments.

Most nations have fire safety considerations built into building design or legislation that must be followed during construction, and then afterwards during the operation of commercial or industrial buildings. You may know these as 'fire codes', 'fire safety law', or other terms. We can't rely on this though, because as we know, shortcuts can often be taken and things aren't always what they appear to be. Often while working at London Fire Brigade's Training School I would be walking to work looking at residential apartments in old buildings wondering about the layouts inside and whether alterations had been made in accordance with these vital laws, or whether they had been adapted and contained nasty surprises and complicated layouts for the firefighters that I trained. It is vital for every firefighter to become familiar with the types of building that exist within their station's (and even the whole department's) local area. This is often referred to as 'knowing the patch', and it is well worth putting in the hard work and taking the time to walk around and really look at the construction in your area.

Buildings can differ vastly – if we take a look at residential premises alone, these can be detached (single family homes), semi-detached (adjoined), terraced (row-houses), apartments (flats), maisonettes (above ground apartments with upper floor(s)), single storey, dual storey, high rise and so on. Let us take a look at a few of these and the hazards they present, and consider how the fire behaviour can influence our tactics.

# Residential buildings

Human factors are obviously a major consideration when assessing a fire in a residential property. First, are persons reported as missing, necessitating rescue, and are there other factors at play such whether doors or windows have been left open when people have escaped from the property. (We'll cover more of that in Chapter 6). The contents and furnishings and the potential 'fire loading' are all relevant here.

## Modern furnishings

You will remember that in Volume 1 we discussed the modernisation of home furnishings and the higher energy loading of most domestic properties, with their capacity for fast development, their ability to use up available air rapidly and to create a 'ventilation controlled' situation with the accompanying risks including backdraft potential. We also looked at the energy of materials versus the practical cooling capabilities of water – how much water it will take to extinguish effectively.

In addition, we should consider that, as most rooms in a usual residential building will be occupied, they will also be furnished, perhaps carpeted. This presents the potential for pyrolysis and the release of flammable gases from those contents should they be affected by heat, which may be transmitted from a fire in an adjoining room, including rooms above or below, or even one remote from it. We should also recognise that 'hoarding' has become more commonplace and properties may be heavily fire loaded making access difficult.

## Room size

Smaller rooms in residential premises, in comparison to commercial buildings, will contain less available air, particular when doors are shut. This too will affect how a fire develops, especially when coupled with higher fire loading. Naturally, a smaller room can use its air supply and become pressurised more quickly than a large one (recall our PVT principles from Volume 1).

That said, with these PVT principles in mind, we should also consider that 'open plan' layouts in residential properties will provide more available air to fires, slowing their transition to becoming ventilation controlled, but providing more air to develop the fire towards flashover and full development. We can see, then, that having an idea as to the layout of a property has important implications for how we approach a fire and what we might expect.

# Attics and cellars

Residential properties often have pitched roofs containing an attic or void. These can sometimes be shared over a number of terraced properties (rowhouses). All such voids can act as reservoirs for fire gases, places where they can accumulate, mix with air and dilute into the flammable range, waiting for an ignition source. **Remember the risk of fire gas ignition (FGI)!** Residential buildings such as those converted into a number of apartments can also have this potential for fire gas accumulation as well as hidden fire spread and complicated layouts.

Older residential buildings may well have basements or cellars (also very common in Scandinavia and Canada), which may contain stored materials or other fire loading as well as heating system boilers and other ignition sources. Should a fire burn in a basement, there is the potential for the heat to cause pyrolysis of materials on the floor above it with risk of FGI, and if there is only one door in and no windows out (at ground level) these can keep burning for some time, but become ventilation controlled with all the attendant hazards. It's also important to remember that if a fire is burning directly under floorboards or joists it can weaken them considerably and raises the very real risk of collapsing floors. This applies to floors above cellars or to any floor above a burning compartment.

As these type of properties will almost certainly have electrical and, potentially, a fuel (gas or oil) supply, consider isolating this at an early stage if safe to do so to prevent adding further complexities and dangers to the fire.

It is also important to remember that in 'traditional construction', if a fire is burning directly under floorboards or joists, it can weaken them considerably and also cause contents on the floor above such as carpets to pyrolyse.

# Windows and doors

Regardless of the size of the room, its role as a 'container' of fire gases may become compromised if windows or doors fail. We can account a little for this though by knowing our ground.

In colder climates such as Scandinavia, residential buildings are designed to keep heat inside through copious insulation and, for example, windows might be triple glazed. This type of window and these buildings are less likely to fail due to the thickness of their walls, windows and their general design, and will keep heat (and fire) inside, limiting the available ventilation from that potential opening.

The opposite is true for warmer climates. My friends Dave Casey in Louisiana and Joe DeVito in Florida have less insulation in their homes in order to keep cool in the higher temperatures. Single-glazed windows are more likely to break under heat stress and provide another source of air to any fire. That said, there is a trend even in warmer climates to increase the insulation when the building contains an air conditioning system. Again, know your ground!

## For firefighters: what considerations are relevant to residential buildings?

- Smaller room sizes in residential buildings can use up available air quickly and move a fire to a ventilation-controlled profile.
- Increased energy contents of materials can also use up available air quickly, changing the fire profile and increasing water/media requirements to extinguish it.
- Furnishings of adjoining or remote rooms affected by heat can pyrolyse and release flammable gases increasing the risk of fire gas ignitions.
- Open plan layouts can increase air availability and increase speed or fire development toward flashover.
- Complicated layouts, spaces and roof voids can present the risks of both hidden fire spread and fire gas accumulation (FGI).
- Hoarding and complicated layouts increase the difficulty in locating a fire, stretching hoses and safe movement, and they also present more fuels to burn.
- Basements can present extreme fire behaviour risks and the potential for rapid collapse if the ceilings are not finished with gypsum board.
- Escaping persons can impede operations.
- Utilities such as gas and electricity can become involved.

# High rise buildings

High rise buildings can be either residential or commercial and present factors that need to be considered from both of those building types a well as the additional issues inherent in tall buildings. In these buildings there are a number of factors that should be taken into account when sizing up for tactical approaches.

With regard to making assessments at high rise buildings there can be a number of risks. Let's examine the fire dynamics factors first.

This comes up in more depth in Chapter 4 that looks at environmental factors, but the phenomena we looked at in Volume 1 – wind-driven fires, the coanda effect and stack effect – are critical considerations when it comes to high rise firefighting.

The coanda effect can result in fire spread to floors above the floor of fire origin, which is essential to know if we have firefighters operating on floors above the fire performing rescues or assisting evacuation. It has the potential to creep up behind us and surprise us.

The stack effect is the natural upward movement of buoyant, heated gases, like in a chimney. These can begin to accumulate if they are not exhausted and can radiate the heat contained, potentially causing further fire spread but also impeding escape and presenting a risk of fire gas ignition. It is crucial to be aware of this, particularly in vertical shafts such as stairwells, garbage chutes and elevator housings. Depending on the height of the building, the 'stack' of smoke may cool and accumulate at a level significantly beneath the very top of the building.

## Figure 3.1: The stack effect in a high-rise building

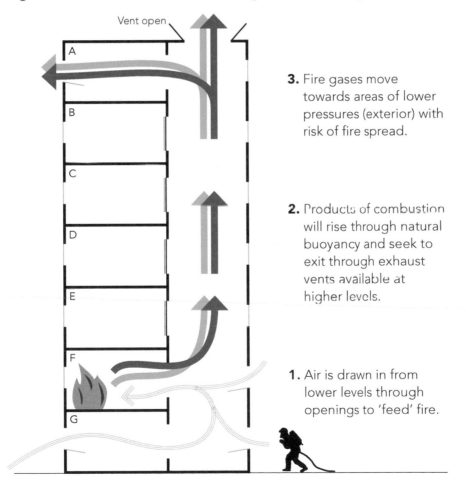

**3.** Fire gases move towards areas of lower pressures (exterior) with risk of fire spread.

**2.** Products of combustion will rise through natural buoyancy and seek to exit through exhaust vents available at higher levels.

**1.** Air is drawn in from lower levels through openings to 'feed' fire.

# Figure 3.2: Stack effect causing accumulation

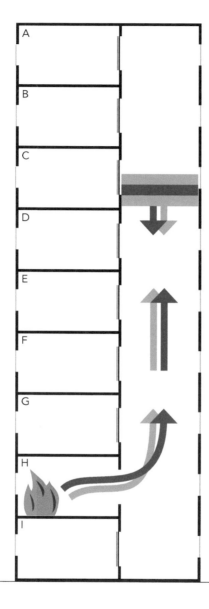

**4.** Due to loss of buoyancy and cooling of fire gases, the shaft above the accumulation may appear 'clear'.

**3.** When the natural buoyancy is exhausted, fire gas/smoke can accumulate at this point, and a 'backfill' can commence.

**2.** While rising, the fire gases mix with air, and cool reducing in buoyancy and volume.

**1.** Products of combustion are drawn into stairwell. Natural buoyancy causes them to rise.

The layout and format of high-rise buildings is as relevant as at any other property. Knowledge of the layout of an apartment complex can assist our operations greatly and help us to also avoid mistakes such as creating additional flowpaths and getting caught in the 'kill zone' (between the fire and its exhaust vent) as has happened tragically before, as we noted in the case study section of Volume 1, Chapter 11.

Layout is also primary to tactical considerations. Our water supply in these buildings will be supplied via a 'rising main' into an attack hose – some of you may know it as a 'standpipe'. While we are going to take an in depth look at water supplies in Volume 3 with Martin, our resident expert, we need to consider the following questions here:

- Do we have enough lengths of hose to reach from the rising main outlet to the furthest point within that floor of the building, allowing us to put out fire in any location?
- Do we have sufficient flow rate to be able to cool the contents and extinguish the fire at its stage of development and fire profile?
- Are pressurised systems/auto ventilation systems/life safety systems in use and are they impacting on our operations?

Certain buildings will have automatic ventilation systems in vertical shafts to counteract the 'stack effect' by allowing it to exhaust. Shafts may also be pressurised from the bottom up or top down which can affect the movement of fire gases.

Finally, any 'through draft' in a stairwell that is moving vertically will create an area of low pressure (or 'venturi effect') as it passes a door that is open to a horizontal floor, which can then 'draw' fire gases towards the shaft, essentially as if it's acting like a giant chimney. This is well worth considering when setting up bridgeheads or forward command points.

## Figure 3.3: The venturi effect

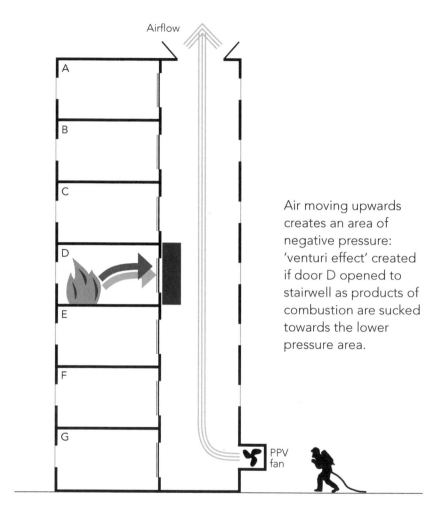

Air moving upwards creates an area of negative pressure: 'venturi effect' created if door D opened to stairwell as products of combustion are sucked towards the lower pressure area.

## For firefighters: what considerations are relevant to high-rise buildings?

Fire dynamics phenomena can have considerable effects, especially:

- Wind driven fires and the blowtorch effect (see Volume 1, Chapter 8 for more details).
- Coanda and stack effects can spread fire and present risks of FGI.
- Knowledge of layouts is crucial to avoid creating flowpaths or getting caught in the 'kill zone', and in ensuring we have enough hose, and sufficient flow, to reach the fire.
- A working knowledge of the fixed installations in the building such as fire engineered systems, pressurisation systems, wet or dry rising or falling mains (standpipes) is essential to be able to avoid deterioration or negative effects on the fire dynamics.
- Consider whether using specialised techniques is appropriate, such as the use of 'floor below nozzles' (see Figure 3.4). These are discussed further in Volume 3.

### Figure 3.4: A floor below nozzle in action

(Image courtesy of West Midlands Fire Service.)

# Commercial buildings (offices and shops)

Commercial buildings may well also share some of the characteristics we've already looked at, especially in metropolitan areas. They may well be in high-rise buildings, for example, in which case all the factors from those are also applicable. They may well share features with residential buildings too, and perhaps even heritage properties (next section). Let's look at some of the risks in commercial buildings.

First, as open-plan offices become more commonplace we should remember that a fire in a commercial building may have a significant area and plentiful supply of air to fuel it. It will therefore have the potential to move towards flashover and full development quickly before using up its available air and becoming ventilation controlled. However, the reverse could also true and that, should smaller rooms or individual offices be in use, these can become ventilation controlled very quickly with the risks of backdraft.

The contents of commercial buildings are of vital importance, too. If we consider offices, they may well contain a significant amount of high-energy release loading such as computers, monitors and other plastics, as well as chemically impregnated furniture which can pyrolyse and release copious volumes of fire gases with a wide flammable range. Shops, meanwhile, can contain significant amounts of fire loading – think about large sporting goods stores with soccer shirts, jerseys and other clothing, for example. The close proximity of the loading can result in a very rapid fire spread.

My personal favourite consideration, so often overlooked at commercial buildings, is that they will almost certainly have a 'false ceiling'. This is a decorative, cosmetic feature that usually conceals electrical cables, ducting and other installations. They are often composed of lightweight tiles that look like the ceiling in Figure 3.5.

## Figure 3.5: A typical commercial ceiling

While these may well have to be fire rated and compliant with fire and building codes, what we have in effect is a large void that can act as a huge reservoir, allowing fire gases to accumulate and, potentially, for fire to spread behind firefighting crews. This type of ceiling presents a huge risk of fire gas ignition.

Premises can contain installations such as heating and ventilation systems, automatic smoke ventilation and also firefighting equipment such as rising mains.

### For firefighters: what considerations are relevant to commercial buildings?

- Commercial premises can carry similar risks as high rise buildings, with fixed installations such as heating and ventilation systems, automatic smoke ventilation and also firefighting equipment such as rising mains.
- Significant fire loading, with technological equipment or large quantities of stock (clothing etc.)
- A large availability of oxygen in open-plan offices will have a significant the effect on fire profile (fuel-controlled potential) meaning the fire will burn for longer, burn hotter and develop further – it may only be limited by the quantity of fuel available to it.
- Less availability of air in smaller offices will have an effect on fire profile meaning it will reach a ventilation controlled profile more quickly with the attendant risks of backdraft.
- Be aware of voids and the potential for fire gas ignition and hidden fire spread.

# Industrial and heritage buildings (warehouses and factories)

Many of the risks these buildings carry can be similar to those of commercial properties as they may well have adjoining office components within.

More modern industrial buildings are usually constructed of steel frames with reinforced concrete floors, while walls can be a block or brick base with a lightweight cladding that covers higher levels and roofs. They can have a very large floor area and extremely large quantities of air available to assist fire development. A fire profile can therefore be fuel controlled and limited only by the available fuel; air is not a problem. However, because of this and the contents held within, there is a potential for extremely high temperatures, heat release rates and speeds of development. The failure of the lightweight cladding, or the fixings securing them, can result in further flowpaths being created, supplying more air, allowing gases to become turbulent and spread more quickly.

Considering the contents and the amount of energy contained within, these buildings will require extremely high water flow rates. The accessibility and ability to supply firefighters with sufficient water is especially important here.

High level racking such as those found in supermarkets and warehouses can have a compartmentalising effect, acting like walls and allowing radiant heat to contribute to fire growth. These can also act as 'channels' allowing a flowpath to develop with potential for high speeds of exiting fire gases.

Due to the large compartment size of industrial buildings, it is possible to have a fire at different stages of development in different areas of the compartment. Fire gases can be at different concentrations throughout the building with potential for ignition. These are known as travelling fires.

Industrial buildings may also be designed to 'fail' in a fire situation so that they collapse in a controlled, or at least predictable, manner. We have already mentioned the steel framework of these buildings, and while protected in certain circumstances with intumescent paints, the can have certain designed 'fail points'. An often-quoted figure of 693°c is the point at which steel loses two thirds of its integrity. A number of other factors are in play here, but always remember the potential for collapse.

Older industrial buildings and heritage properties also present increased collapse risks, dryer linings and the potential for years of contents to absorb into walls and floors, especially distilleries and warehouses where solvents may have been used. These can all contribute to the faster development of a fire, and old fashioned methods such as 'lathe and plaster'[2] can also conceal hidden fire spread. The elements of a structure here, such as old cast iron columns and beams, and stone columns, can be susceptible to 'thermal shock' and collapse if they are suddenly cooled by the application of a firefighting water jet.

Industrial buildings may also contain 'LISPS' (Light Insulated Sandwich Panels). LISPS can be used as sterile surfaces in buildings such as refrigeration plants or where pharmaceuticals are in use. When exposed to fire, they can delaminate, produce extremely toxic smoke and high temperatures and conceal fire spread behind the panel's facing. Due to the high-energy heat release, they can also impact upon structural integrity by affecting structurally important elements.

---

2    Lathe and plaster is an old fashioned way of plastering internal walls using very thin strips of wood (lathes) that are plastered onto – as such, they can hide voids behind them.

**For firefighters: what considerations are relevant to industrial and heritage buildings?**

- Vast floor spaces – copious availability of air for fires.
- Heavy fire loading requiring large quantities of water to cool.
- Easy failure of lightweight construction components increasing airflows and turbulence.
- Racking and contents can have a 'compartmentalising effect'.
- Fires at different stages of development can exist in different areas of the building.
- Gases can exist at different concentrations throughout the building.
- Increased potential for collapse (including designed failure points).
- Rapid fire development caused by contents (localised flashover potential).
- Hidden fire spread in heritage buildings due to construction techniques.
- LISPS (Light Insulated Sandwich Panels).

# Sprinklers, dampers, ducting, drenchers: a look at fixed installations

Applicable to all of these building types, sprinklers, dampers, ducting and drenchers should be considered when making an assessment of a building – they can give us valuable indicators, or can mislead us.

If sprinklers are operating in the building, it is a valuable indicator of the location of a fire, however the sprinkler's water application and effect on the fire may give a false impression. For example, the steam created when water from a sprinkler head is projected onto burning materials can be mistaken for 'white' fire gas. It is important to not be misled by this, as we know from Volume 1, smoke is dangerous regardless of the colour or temperature and should always be regarded as fuel.

Ducting and air conditioning systems can also allow fire gases to move around a building and accumulate in other areas and spread fire. This should be accounted for or at least considered when making an initial assessment. Simply ask two questions: are these installations in the building? Could the fire have spread?

These systems are nowadays fitted with devices called 'dampers' to prevent gases from spreading. They operate by being linked to the automatic fire detection system, or stand-alone like a sprinkler, but when their operation is triggered, either by an auto system or a certain temperature being reached, they act like a blind or shutter and seal the duct or pipework to prevent fire gas movement. While they are very useful in controlling the spread of fire gases, in this situation you could still have a duct full of fire gas within its flammable range.

## Aide memoire: Building

| Building Factor | Flashover | Backdraft | Fire Gas Ignition |
|---|---|---|---|
| **Type of construction** Construction materials, thermal properties & geometry has an enormous influence on fire development & structural stability.<br><br>**Use and occupancy** Gives an indication of the likely life risk, fuel type/load<br><br>**Stage of development**<br><br>**Fire profile**<br><br>**Structural integrity** | Flashover will occur in most buildings if sufficient air is available.<br><br>Lightweight single pane windows/doors may fail and allow sufficient air for flashover to occur.<br><br>Large open plan with limited compartmentation will allow rapid spread.<br><br>Heavy brick or cement rendered walls will absorb a lot of energy, which could delay flashover. | Backdraft is more likely in energy efficient buildings with good insulation and sealed openings such as double/triple glazed windows.<br><br>Developing fires may consume the available oxygen before it can transition to fully developed.<br><br>Heat indicators may be less obvious due to the superior insulation associated with this type of construction. | Voids, ducts, shafts, large open plan, high false or suspended ceilings etc. allow smoke to be transported & accumulate in areas adjacent to, or some distance from, the compartment of origin.<br><br>Poor or damaged smoke/fire stopping may be found in original or modified buildings.<br><br>The unburnt fuel in the smoke is partially mixed with fresh air and can accumulate to flammable concentrations.<br><br>Conducted heat may pyrolyse combustible elements/linings in spaces adjacent to the room of origin. |

# Chapter 4:
# Reading fire step
# 2 – environmental
# considerations

Considering BE-SAHF, having looked at the **B** – buildings – we must now turn our attention to the **E** – the environment. We have already begun to take into account environmental factors while thinking about types of buildings, structure, contents and the impact for fires within them. Most firefighters would immediately think of weather conditions as being environmental factors and they would be right, but let's go back to geography class and think about these factors in a wider context.

If we look at the wider environment, there are many factors that are relevant to our scene assessment and tactical decision making. Initially, it is worth considering the density of the landscape. Are we dealing with an incident that is relatively standalone, or are we operating in a built-up environment with surrounding or adjoining risks where radiant heat could cause fire spread to other buildings not yet involved? Naturally, if we consider that a fire could spread then we may require further resources and an increased attendance to protect other buildings. This will also impact on your plans depending on your fire department's staffing and how long will it take for reinforcements to arrive etc.

The flip-side of this coin is that a fire in a location that is isolated may present other difficulties. More rural or non-urban environments could be some distance from hydrants, mains and water supplies, and we therefore need to consider the availability of water to implement effective operations. Is there enough water in the fire truck's tank to successfully extinguish the fire? Or will we need to supplement our supply? Isolated environments also amplify the logistical difficulties of getting firefighters and other resources onto the scene with increased response times and the impact on what we can do.

So, having looked at the background aspects of environmental factors that are an important part of an assessment, let's look at the factors that directly impact upon the fire and what effect they can have, and the overlap with the wider definition of 'environment', too.

There are a number of weather events that can have an impact upon a fire's development and profile, including rain, snow, ice, temperature and wind. Of course, depending on where you are in the world you may be more familiar with certain of these conditions than others, but it's vital to have a good understanding of all of them. Let's start with the wind.

## Wind

There is a significant overlap between wider environmental considerations and the wind. Urban or built up environments can affect the wind in two ways: buildings can be shielded from wind by other buildings, and deflections from taller buildings can add frictional drag, turbulence and eddies – areas of low pressure on the 'leeward', or protected, side of the building, opposite to the side the wind is pushing against, the 'windward' side (Figure 4.1).

Being aware of these low pressure areas is vital given what we know from Volume 1 about fire gases moving from areas of high pressure to areas of lower pressure. Furthermore, wind direction and speed is critical when planning ventilation operations – this is explored further in Volume 3.

### Figure 4.1: Eddies

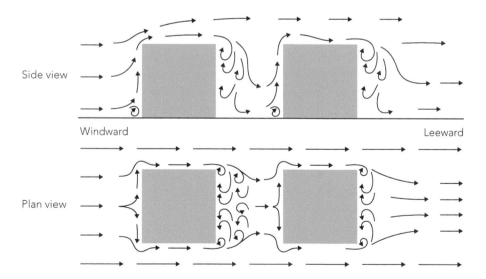

Side view

Windward                                                    Leeward

Plan view

## Figure 4.2: Wind and pressure

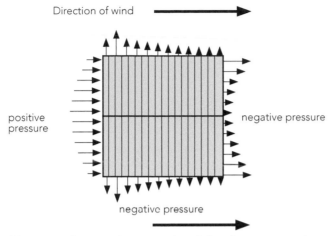

Direction of wind

positive pressure

negative pressure

negative pressure

The distribution of pressure round a building, seen from above.

(©Per Hardestam. Reprinted with kind permission.)

## Figure 4.3: Wind direction and pressure

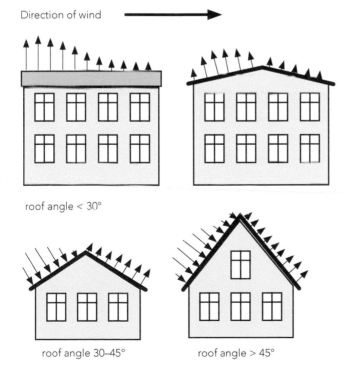

Direction of wind

roof angle < 30°

roof angle 30–45°

roof angle > 45°

The distribution of pressure over a flat roof. There is normally negative pressure over the entire surface of the roof.

The distribution of pressure over a gable roof. The pressure varies from negative pressure to positive pressure, depending on the angle of the roof and where on the roof one is.

(©Per Hardestam. Reprinted with kind permission.)

Buildings that are fairly evenly spaced can also create wind channels or tunnels where the wind moves at faster speeds, a version of the venturi effect in a way (uninterrupted by buildings and turbulence). For example, the grid system of buildings in Chicago creates these wind tunnels where the wind from Lake Michigan can pick up speed and is amplified (Figure 4.4).

## Figure 4.4: Wind tunnel effect

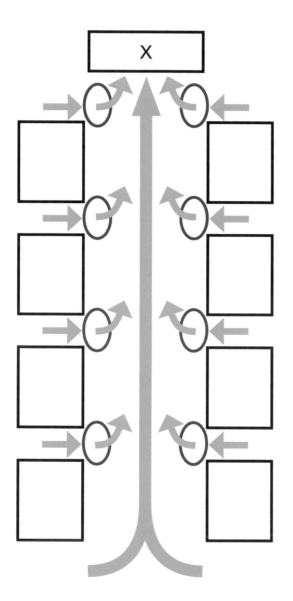

The main direction of wind is towards the target building marked 'X'.

Low pressure area created which 'sucks' in wind.

Wind moves towards, or is deflected into the main channel increasing velocity.

These situations can lead firefighters to encounter high speed winds and we must account for them in our assessment and the effect that it can have on fires.

Wind driven fires (see Volume 1, Chapter 8) can occur where there has been either a failure of a door/window or an opening created on the windward face of an affected building, with the result that the wind is blowing straight into it. If this blows straight into the fire compartment and it is otherwise sealed with the door shut, or the total available space is relatively small, then this opening will be acting as both the inlet for air driven in at speed by the wind, but also the outlet or exhaust for fire gases – a bidirectional flowpath (see Volume 1, p10).

But, you ask, how does the fire gas exhaust from this opening if it is 'sealed' by the wind blowing into it and around it? Put simply, and non-scientifically, the pressure of the fire gases will continue to increase (remember our PVT principles) until they reach a high enough pressure that they can temporarily overcome the pressure of the wind and exhaust. In appearance, this looks like a 'belching' or occasional 'coughing' of fire gases and is an indicator of a wind driven fire.

It is absolutely risk critical to consider that any creation of an exhaust vent on the downwind, or leeward, side of the fire will almost certainly result in the creation of a unidirectional flowpath with the wind driving fire and products towards the created opening at high speeds and with high levels of heat release. This is also known as the 'blowtorch effect' and has caught out many firefighters in the past.

We should also remember that wind can cause external fire spread to be rapid, and while we are focused on compartment firefighting, we should learn a lesson from our brothers and sisters in wildfire firefighting and realise that adjacent risks can soon become involved if this is not considered.


## Temperature

Following many discussions and consultations, we found that in order for external temperatures and conditions to start having a visible effect on conditions, we would have to be operating in extremely cold conditions, so this may only really apply to those of you reading in Alaska, Canada, Scandinavia and other colder climates. For the rest of us, unless there is a huge spectrum and difference in temperatures between the warmest you encounter and the lowest, then the impact on the appearance of BE-SAHF indicators is unlikely to be noticeable.

Edinburgh University's Fire Dynamics faculty were kind enough to succinctly state: *'Cold temperatures won't have a major effect on smoke plume appearance.'*

What we did uncover though, via the UK's CFBT 'Godfather' Paul Grimwood, and from prior conversations with Swedish fire engineer J Mandre, was that, taking our PVT principles from Volume 1, a 40 Kelvin (40°c) difference in air temperature (T) alters (V) volume by 14.3%. Put simply, this means that air at 0°c will contain almost 15% more oxygen than air at 40°c (Grimwood, 2008, p299). Cold air, if admitted to the fire by making openings or by firefighter entry, can therefore lead to a more rapid development of the fire than would be the case at the higher temperatures due to the increased oxygen content. Paul and Mr Mandre go on to say that the colder temperatures have a negligible cooling effect as they enter the building or structure.

So, for most climates, we may encounter a danger of increased fire development speeds due to increased oxygen content during the coldest days of our winters compared to the hottest days of our summers. Taking a wider perspective, however, we should be paying attention to the flowpaths we are creating and managing, regardless of the external temperatures.

## Moisture

Moisture in the air or atmosphere will also have an effect upon fire development, acting as a passive agent and absorbing heat until it reaches its thermal capacity. Higher levels of humidity in the atmosphere will reduce the ability of moisture in the fuel to readily evaporate to air. As a very crude rule of thumb, the higher the humidity, the harder it is for fuel to dry.

Obviously, when a fuel is drying out and moisture ($H_2O$) is being expelled in the form of water vapour or steam, the appearance of this will be seen in the fire gases. Using wood as an example, the transition from pyrolysis in the incipient stage of fire development – where $H_2O$ and $CO_2$ are emitted – to the stage where CO is pyrolysed and ignited can be extremely rapid given sufficient ventilation.

A lot moisture can give an impression that there is a lot of fire gas, or, conversely, lull us into a false sense of security if what we assume is steam is in fact 'white smoke' from other burning materials. These factors should be considered by the thoughtful and dynamic incident commander if dampness and moisture could be a factor.

Bear in mind when operating internally, however, that with use of insulation and internal heating, interior compartments that are usually occupied will be less likely to have damp and humidity acting on the contents unless exposed by open windows or other openings. In derelict or unoccupied buildings, such as those with leaking roofs, broken windows etc., this becomes a more relevant factor. Although of course, it may be counterbalanced by having less contents and fire loading contained within.

## For firefighters: what considerations are relevant to environmental conditions?

- Geographical location – consider what environment you are operating in (urban/rural) and how this will impact on response times for reinforcements, availability of water supplies and proximity to other risks? All of these influence our tactics and size up.
- Wind impact – velocity and direction – remember that conditions may lend themselves to the potential for wind-driven fires.
- Check for signs and symptoms of wind-driven fires being exhibited ('belching' fire gases).
- Analyse whether the landscape could amplify the effects of the wind, such as in Chicago's 'wind channels'.
- Note which is the upwind side and therefore safest to attack from if possible.
- Consider the requirement for specialised equipment (e.g. floor below nozzles).
- Very low temperatures means that air has a higher oxygen content, so extra caution should be exercised when managing flowpaths or admitting air after creating openings.
- Humid conditions may be reducing the pyrolysis of moisture and drying of the fuel affecting the visible signs of fire development, but this can rapidly alter and progress. This is infrequent and is affected heavily by building type.
- Very low humidity alone will not have a significant impact on development or visible fire behaviour indicators, but it can increase the impact of a wind driven fire.

## Aide memoire

| Indicator | All rapid fire developments (flashover, backdraft, FGI) |
|---|---|
| Wind velocity & Wind direction | This factor can play a major role in the rate and direction of fire spread. The velocity will magnify the effects of low humidity and extremes of temperature.<br><br>The natural lay of the land or the built environment around the structure can cause variations in direction and velocity of the wind on the various sides of the involved structure.<br><br>The 'wind-driven fire' scenario is an example of how external wind conditions can have an extreme effect on fire behaviour.<br><br>It is critical to consider wind direction and velocity before making any openings. |
| Low humidity | Prolonged low humidity conditions can dry vegetation to a 'cured' state. This increases the potential ignitability of surrounding vegetation and accumulated leaf litter in gutters and around the outside of the structure.<br><br>A similar effect can influence the rate of ignitibility and spread of structure components, and even contents to lesser extent. This effect is exacerbated by hot and/or high wind velocity. |
| Extreme heat | Fighting operations can become extremely arduous in these conditions and frequent relieves combined with core cooling may be essential to rehabilitate crews.<br><br>Extra vigilance is required to prevent heat stress and dehydration. |
| Extreme cold | Rapid cooling of discharged smoke may decrease its buoyancy. When combined with 'low atmospheric pressure' an inversion layer can form that will prevent the smoke from rising.<br><br>The construction commonly found in areas likely to experience extreme cold are less likely to show heat indicators that could be considered 'common, normal or reliable' in tropical/sub-tropical climates.<br><br>Firefighter welfare in these conditions requires knowledge and Standard Operational Procedures (SOPs) based on experience. This is business as usual for departments that commonly experience extreme cold.<br><br>The highest risk exists when these conditions occur as part of a 'rare extreme' event in areas that are not experienced in dealing with extreme cold. |

# Chapter 5:
# Reading fire step 3
# – smoke

Smoke is perhaps the most visible indicator that we experience following our arrival upon a scene, and often on approach to the incident ground and it can give us vital early clues about what's going on in a building. So, what can it tell us and what are we looking for?

If we recall what we learnt in Volume 1, we know the following:

- Smoke is a fuel, consisting of flammable gases and unburned products of pyrolysis.

- Smoke is a combination of gases that are at a higher pressure than atmosphere so it will move towards areas of lower pressure.

- Smoke is naturally buoyant, so will rise. It will become more buoyant as temperature increases and so does pressure! (Remember your PVT principles.)

- Again, considering the PVT principles, as the temperature increases the smoke/gas will expand and increase its volume.

- If the volume becomes fixed (a compartment is closed for example) and the temperature still rises, the pressure of smoke/fire gases continues to increase.

- The point at which exiting smoke that is 'overpressure' meets entering air that is 'underpressure' is known as a 'neutral plane' or 'smoke layer'. This can provide clues to the stage of a fire's development and its ventilation profile. Is it low, lowering, high or bouncing?

- The consistency, velocity and colour of smoke can be affected by the materials burning and the spread of the fire or availability of air.

- Smoke/fire gases have a flammable range – points between a maximum concentration of fuel to air and a minimum concentration of fuel to air, between which they will burn, with an ideal mixture ratio where they will burn most forcefully. The concentration of this range – 'lean' or 'rich' – can affect its appearance and should influence tactics.

Taking these points, what can we learn when we are conducting a size up? What exactly are we looking for when observing smoke?

If we begin our observation on arrival, the first thing that is often apparent is the volume of smoke that presents itself. If a significant quantity of smoke is exiting from the building it can suggest that a fire has spread or that a lot of contents/fuel is involved. A basic principle of smoke is that the more complete the combustion, the less smoke is produced. If the fire is burning efficiently, usually where air is unlimited and readily available, less smoke will be produced than in a ventilation controlled fire where it has a limited air supply.

## Smoke location versus fire location

We must remember that smoke location is different from fire location, although it can be a clue to help us find the fire. Using our basic scientific knowledge and that precious fire service commodity of common sense, we can assume that higher pressure gas is moving towards areas of lower pressure, and we can use our imaginations to work backwards, or 'upstream', against the smoke and make a calculation of where the smoke is originating from.

Thermal image cameras are very useful in assessing smoke as the velocity, buoyancy and movement can be viewed with some clarity, allowing us to check exiting smoke temperatures and providing information as to conditions inside. Thermal image cameras also allow us to identify heat signatures, but we'll come to that in Volume 3 with a lesson on tactical thermal imaging.

As we examined in Chapter 3, fixed installations and voids create routes which can allow smoke to travel and accumulate in some quantity away from the room of the fire's origin. When this happens, the smoke may cool as it travels further from the heat source and mixes with cooler air, however it can still remain, or even be diluting into its flammable range, just requiring a source to ignite it in a fire gas ignition.

A contained volume of smoke can also provide indicators as to the fire condition. Windows may be completely blackened or obscured by smoke, which indicates that the neutral plane/smoke layer has fallen beneath the level of the window. This may indicate that they fire has become ventilation controlled or limited. This can mean that a fire has either become 'contained', or ventilation controlled, presenting the risk of inducing a backdraft should air be admitted in an uncontrolled manner.

# Smoke layer/neutral plane indicators

The level of the neutral plane/smoke layer can also offer other, vital clues here too.

If the neutral plane is high:

- The fire might be in its early stages of development.
- Smoke might be exiting through a high exhaust vent.

If the neutral plane rises quickly:

- Ventilation may have taken place, either a failure of windows or doors, or due to the fire crew's tactics.

If the neutral plane is lowering:

- Steady lowering indicates the progression of the fire towards flashover.
- Rapid lowering indicates that flashover is approaching imminently due to the intensification of the fire.

If the neutral plane is very low:

- A ventilation controlled profile has occurred and the admission of air could lead to backdraft.

If the neutral plane is 'bouncing':

- A ventilation controlled profile is causing the fire to become starved of oxygen and restrict burning. This leads to smoke cooling and contracting, with the consequential rise in the neutral plane (PVT), which can then lead to negative pressures 'sucking' air in, allowing combustion, increased temperatures, expansion of gases (PVT), and a lowering of the neutral plane again.

The images in Figure 5.1 show the neutral plane altering in a fuel-controlled (copious air available) profile.

## Figure 5.1: An altering neutral plane

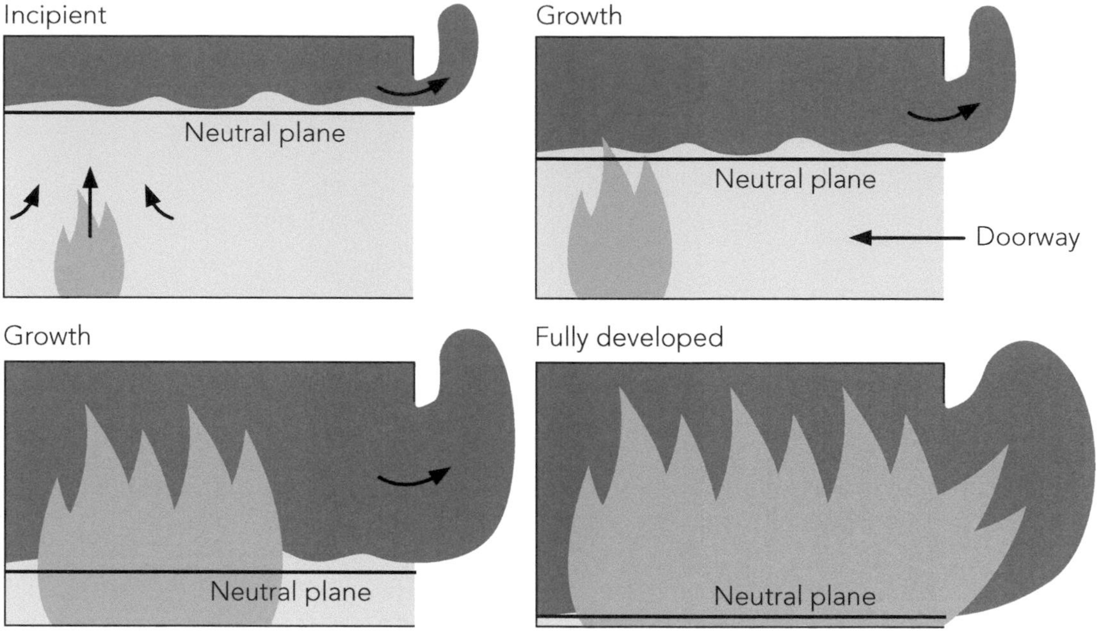

Incipient

Neutral plane

Growth

Neutral plane

Doorway

Growth

Neutral plane

Fully developed

Neutral plane

# Smoke movement indicators

The movement, velocity and pressure of smoke are also valuable indicators of the stage of development and risks of the fire we are sizing up.

When smoke/fire gas is pushing out of gaps under pressure, or pulsing out of openings, it is telling us that it wants to 'breathe' – it desires more air to burn more freely. This is another indication of a ventilation controlled fire situation, where there is a clear and viable risk of backdraft occurring.

Another indicator of this type of ventilation controlled profile, but also indicative of extremely high temperatures, is where smoke exits from a building and suddenly ignites. In this case, the smoke leaves the compartment and, hitting the air outside, dilutes into its flammable range. Because it is also extremely hot and at its auto-ignition temperature it will then ignite and burn off, hence the flames. If these are seen, there is a strong clue that a ventilation controlled profile with extremely high temperatures has occurred inside – exceptionally dangerous conditions and our tactics should reflect this.

# Smoke colour indicators

Smoke colour has been a controversial topic for as long as firefighters have been around. There are a number of interpretations with regard to smoke colour alterations from 'filtering', adhesion of carbon molecules and more.

Scientific explanations around changes in smoke colour are extremely complex and involve hydrocarbon bonding with atmospheric oxygen molecules and free radical interaction, and I would recommend those wanting to learn more about the in-depth science to follow my friend Professor Stefan Svensson through social media as he is eminently more knowledgeable and qualified than I am to inform and teach you in advanced fire dynamics science.

On a basic level, however, and back onto my playing field of the fireground, what can we broadly interpret from smoke colour?

If we observe alterations in the colour and composition of smoke, we can understand that some action is taking place that is affecting the fire:

■ The fire is spreading and more materials are involved, with a different chemical composition.

■ The available air has become restricted and the profile has changed from fuel controlled to ventilation controlled – the fire gases are now too rich to burn having moved out of their flammable range and flaming combustion may no longer be occurring, but heat is still present, causing pyrolysis.

■ The reverse of the above – a failure of a window, or an opening created may have provided additional air and reduced the extent that the fire is limited by available air, or even altered its profile to fuel controlled, allowing combustion to occur more freely or even without restriction.

■ An intervention is taking place where an extinguishing agent is being applied to the fire, surfaces, or is having a cooling effect on the smoke (fire gases). Has a sprinkler system activated for example?

Let's examine each of these in slightly more detail.

## The fire is spreading and more materials are involved, with a different chemical composition

We know that materials are simply combinations of chemical constituents and that pyrolysis causes the breakdown of these materials into these constituents, releasing them into fire gases. These constituents can release coloured gases when they burn. For example, the pyrolysis of wood/cellulose can release a yellow or brown smoke, so changes in that colour, perhaps to green or blue, suggest that they are now being affected by other burning products that are releasing gases in different colours, blending with them and displaying changes of colour to the observant firefighter. As more products are now burning, it is a strong suggestion that the fire has spread.

While it is true that different chemicals and substances will burn with different coloured smoke, anecdotal experience shows that, with a few rare exceptions, white smoke is produced while the fuel is pyrolysing. This moves onto the shades of grey (light to dark) while there is enough air for active combustion. Fuel packages tend to release black smoke when they become very ventilation limited (but there is still enough air to allow for a poor flaming combustion or active smouldering combustion).

Generally, in compartment fires we have a mixture of materials. Unless we are operating in an industrial context where large quantities of a particular product are being stored, colours generated will be a combination created from a mixture of fuel products.

**In general, smoke colour gives us an ideas of how efficient the combustion process is:**

- **Grey – good to fair combustion so a reasonable air supply.**

- **Black – very ventilation limited but still burning or at least smouldering well.**

- **White – pyrolysis is taking place but the fire is just developing, or, if the air supply to a developed fire gets cut off totally, even smouldering becomes hindered and it switches back to pyrolysis.**

Products that chemically consist of hydrocarbons can produce a dark smoke, but, if we remember our signs and symptoms of potential backdraft, we will recall that a very rich, dark smoke, often blackening windows, is a sign of a ventilation controlled fire.

# The available air has become restricted and the profile has changed from fuel controlled to ventilation controlled – the fire gases are now too rich to burn having moved out of their flammable range and flaming combustion may no longer be occurring, but heat is still present causing pyrolysis

When flaming combustion occurs, carbon particles (soot) are released into the smoke and present a very dark colour. When temperatures drop below a level where flaming combustion can occur, pyrolysis will continue but carbon molecules remain on/within the fuel package. Grimwood *et al* (2005) states that this type of pyrolysis also occurs, 'when oxygen concentration drops below a 15% ratio to fuel'. This leads to lighter, even white smoke being produced, which contains very high levels of unburned fuel.

The presence of light-coloured smoke can occur where heat is conducted or transferred to adjoining or adjacent compartments, causing pyrolysis without flaming combustion, and this should be a warning of the potential for fire gas ignition. Figure 5.2 indicates that although the smoke is very white, it is still full of a high level of fuel and can easily ignite with the introduction of an ignition source.

Firefighters attending basement fires should remain ultra-aware of the potential for this type of event to occur. Unless a basement has ventilation points such as 'basement lights', a fire may well have a very limited supply of air to it, becoming ventilation controlled. However, the presence of heat without the flaming combustion can continue to cause pyrolysis and release white smoke, not only from the materials involved but those on the floor above the heat source. A tragic incident occurred in 2004 at Bethnal Green Road in London where two London Fire Brigade firefighters, Adam Meere and Billy Faust, sadly lost their lives in the line of duty attending a basement fire.

While we examined the fire behaviour at this incident in Volume 1 (p82), we did not revisit the narrative from official reports. While delivering the official case study to LFB staff as an instructor at London's Training School (Academy), I noted that incident communications to control clearly indicate that this type of white smoke was observed on scene on the ground and upper floors. We should continue to honour FF Meere and FF Faust by interpreting the cause of this white smoke and adopting the relevant levels of caution in our tactics.

# The reverse of the above – a failure of a window, or an opening created may have provided additional air and reduced the extent that the fire is limited by available air, or even altered its profile to fuel controlled, allowing combustion to occur more freely or even without restriction

Should a change in conditions be observed, it may be the case that an element has failed, or an opening has been created that has allowed burning to take place. A darkening may occur in the visible smoke. As with all of these considerations, these should be looked at in conjunction with other factors. The creation of an opening allowing an inlet flowpath to supply air to the fire will also be accompanied by a rise in the neutral plane.

# An intervention is taking place where an extinguishing agent is being applied to the fire, surfaces, or is even having a cooling effect on the smoke (fire gases). Has a sprinkler system activated for example?

Sprinkler activation generally keeps a fire in check or prevents further development, unless it activates in the incipient stages of development in which case it may extinguish the fire. As with any fire, uncontrolled water application to surfaces and linings can result in steam creation at 100°c/212F and this may present itself to those sizing up from the outside. Bear in mind that this can be potentially misleading and a fire of some severity could be in progress within. Don't turn sprinkler mains off without considering this!

As an overall consideration, we should recognise that smoke conditions can present differently from different openings, faces and areas in even the smallest building. Rich, dark smoke may be visible on one face of the building, while white smoke can be seen through a window on the opposing face of the building, even sometimes on the same side.

## For firefighters, what do smoke conditions tell us?

■ Smoke location is not a reliable indicator of fire location, but can present clues. We must remain aware that 'travel' may have taken place.

■ Dark smoke is generally an indicator of limited ventilation to fires and can signpost that gases have moved above their flammable range into a 'too rich' concentration of fuel to air.

■ White/lighter colour smoke can be fuel-rich pyrolysis products created by non-flaming combustion in a fire compartment, or the heat from the fire compartment causing pyrolysis in adjacent areas – classic examples being floors above basements. This indicates a strong potential for rapid fire development (fire gas ignition).

■ Neutral plane positioning can indicate the burning profile and stage of fire development plus the potential for rapid fire developments.

■ Smoke pressures and velocity can indicate high temperatures, burning profile and the potential for a rapid fire development (backdraft).

■ Remote auto ignitions of smoke indicate high temperatures and a rich concentration of fire gases, so oxygen/air must be a critical consideration.

■ Changes in air supply (air admitted or restricted) can affect smoke colour.

■ Fire spread can be indicated by changes in smoke colour.

■ Smoke can present differently in different locations even in small buildings.

■ Fixed installations operating, like sprinklers, can alter visible smoke/fire gases and conceal the true nature of the fire.

## Which factors should we be looking for with smoke?

■ Location/volume.

■ Colour.

■ Buoyancy.

■ Thickness (optical density).

■ Neutral plane levels.

## Aide memoire: Smoke

| Indicator | Flashover | Backdraft | Fire Gas Ignition |
|---|---|---|---|
| **Volume and location**<br><br>Varies with the size of the fire, room geometry, duration of fire, and air supply. | Can be unreliable as a single indicator. Must be read with the other indicators that are present in the fire compartment itself. | Large volumes of smoke will be concentrated in the fire compartment. Other parts of building may have a variety of smoke conditions. Unreliable unless read with other indicators. | Smoke can emerge and accumulate some distance from the source. This can give a false indicator of the location of the fire compartment. |
| **Colour**<br><br>Varies with fuel, type (natural or synthetic) and form (gas, liquid, solid, shavings, dust).<br><br>**Fire profile:**<br>Fuel controlled or ventilation controlled | Flashover requires a reasonable air supply so the smoke will show evidence of flaming combustion which means it will have soot present giving a grey to dark grey colour. As the fire gets closer to flashover it may become fuel controlled which will darken the colour of the smoke towards black. | White smoke may indicate the contents are undergoing pyrolysis and not flaming or smouldering combustion. Yellow/brown can indicate decomposition of wood. Black will generally indicate at least active smouldering combustion of energy rich products. | Smoke that has travelled some distance from the fire compartment may appear lighter in colour due to partial mixing with cooler air as it moves through the structure. |

| Indicator | Flashover | Backdraft | Fire Gas Ignition |
|---|---|---|---|
| **Buoyancy**<br>Hot smoke rapidly rises. | Buoyancy increases as the compartment approaches flashover. Smoke emerging some distance from the room of origin will be less buoyant. | Buoyant, expanding smoke indicates higher internal temperature and pressure – possibility of auto-ignition. Less buoyant (lazy smoke) indicates lower temperature but is still dangerous! | Generally, not very buoyant due to cooling from premixing with the cooler ambient air. |
| **Thickness**<br>Optical/ visual density. | Becomes thicker as flashover approaches. | Usually thick. When at a high temperature it will expand and roll at a high velocity. | Can often appear to be thinner (to some extent) due to pre mixing with cooler, fresh air. |
| **Height of neutral plane**<br>Smoke layer/air interface. | Pre-flashover height is high and rapidly lowers as flashover becomes imminent. | Low or at floor level in the compartment of origin. 'Bouncing' neutral plane can indicate this too. | Usually not well defined due to premixing with cool air. |

# Chapter 6: Reading fire step 4 – air factors

We have already touched upon the influence of air supply, or lack of it, upon fires and our ability to read them. Put simply, the presence of air is going to have a huge effect on the fire condition, its profile (fuel or ventilation controlled) and our tactical decision making.

To revise again, flowpaths can be 'inlet flowpaths' taking air supply to the fire, or 'outlet flowpaths' taking fire gases (smoke) products of combustion away from the fire. They can be 'bidirectional', with the same opening acting as both inlet and outlet, or 'unidirectional', where air comes in through one opening, and smoke/fire gas exits through another. There can also be elements of both, primarily one or the other. If we examine this, taking a simple approach, let's look at what is going in (air) and what is coming out (smoke/fire gas).

We know from Volume 1 that if a rich smoke is coming out of a bidirectional flowpath, the air moving in underneath it may cause some mixing around the level of the neutral plane and dilute it into its flammable range, presenting the risk of fire gases igniting. This mixing of air with the neutral plane may be more turbulent the closer to the fire and heat source we are. If the interface is smooth and appears gentle, combined with white or light smoke, it could be a symptom of potential fire gas ignition.

It is also important to consider which direction these flowpaths are moving from and towards. My great friend and mentor Chief Bobby Halton, Editor-in-Chief of *Fire Engineering* magazine appropriated the military term 'kill zone' to refer to extremely dangerous situations on the fireground. During our discussions, with Bobby's blessing, I applied the kill zone terminology to a specific position within a structure fire and used my own definition:

*'Any position between a fire and an exhaust vent, on the outlet flowpath.'*

(Walker, 2016)

For more information about the kill zone, see Volume 1, but in short, this is a place you don't want to be. Always be aware of where gases are exiting and avoid it!

It's important to remember that even with fire gases largely exiting from an exhaust vent, this may only account for 90%, 80%, or even less, of the fire gases and pyrolysis products, the remainder of which can accumulate or move through any position. These are trying to exit or move to areas of lower pressure, although not through the obvious exhaust vent. There could therefore be more than one kill zone, and this could be any area within a structure or hostile environment that contains unburnt fuel in smoke/gaseous form. Specifically, areas that lie between the point of entry into a structure and the internal position from which the crew are able to apply extinguishing media to the burning surfaces, or directly control the fire through ventilation techniques such as closing doors.

As we have just indicated, an opening can act as both the inlet flowpath and the outlet flowpath. In these circumstances, we may have no alternative but to enter the kill zone in order to make progress towards the fire. However, we can take steps to reduce the risks presented here by moving effectively and using our '3D' nozzle techniques, which are covered in *Volume 3: Fighting Fire*.

Of course, the most dangerous kill zone is when a unidirectional flowpath has been established (inlet flowpath with air feeding the fire from one side and fire gases exhausting along an outlet flowpath on the other side of the fire). In these circumstances it is absolutely essential that fire crews do not position themselves between the fire and the exhaust vent on the outlet flowpath. Doing this unwittingly has resulted in many tragic line of duty deaths. In fact, this area of the kill zone could even be termed the 'suicide zone'. Bobby Halton himself refers to this position as the 'fatal funnel'.

In certain situations, especially where the wind is driving the inlet flowpath, this can even create the 'blowtorch' effect (see Volume 1, Chapter 8) and amplify and accelerate fire development and flame speeds towards crews with deadly effects. This is discussed in depth in Volume 1, but to summarise, the blowtorch effect is where a unidirectional flowpath is created that is amplified by the wind, which strongly acts on the inlet side of the flowpath, driving air into the fire and increasing the speed of exiting fire and fire gases towards their outlet. Between the fire and its exhaust vent is the most dangerous place to be in structural firefighting, particularly in these conditions. It is well deserving of being named the kill zone.

Given the seriousness of the potential risks above, we can see how air and established or created flowpaths are critical to the size up and the tactical decisions we make. This can be as simple as influencing which side of a building we make entry from to avoid entering the kill zone if avoidable.

We can use unidirectional flowpaths to our advantage in forced ventilation operations whereby the swift removal of smoke by management of a unidirectional flowpath, powered by ventilation fans from the inlet side may result in some local fire intensification/growth, but should allow a speedier attack. The trade-off, however, is that the continued air supply to the fire will continue to allow it to develop and intensify, maybe moving more quickly towards flashover. Obviously, utilising these tactics for the wrong burning profile or misjudging the stage of fire development can have catastrophic consequences. This is explored further in Volume 3.

The reverse of this technique can also be helpful. We may decide to restrict the air supply to a fire by closing doors or using smoke curtains to implement an 'anti-ventilation' strategy to assist our tactics. This is also explored in more depth in Volume 3.

Multiple flowpaths can cause turbulence in fire gas flows, mixing into their flammable range and creating a cocktail of fire behaviour conditions inside, with the potential for rapid developments and increased burning velocities, large surface area flame fronts and other dangerous situations.

Externally, we should also look for the 'sucking' of air into a building. Thermal imaging cameras can assist in seeing this movement. As with smoke pulsing, then 'sucking' the air, this can indicate a ventilation controlled fire with backdraft potential. Rapid pulsations can indicate extremely high temperatures and pressures (PVT principles) and a very nasty surprise if we admit air in an uncontrolled manner. The 'belch' that we see in wind-driven situations can show a fleeting transition from a seemingly unidirectional outlet to a unidirectional inlet. This is another indicator of a ventilation controlled profile and the risk of backdraft. Finally, some firefighters may hear a whistling/sucking sound as gases are sucked in following pulsation of fire gases from small gaps. This is another indicator of a ventilation controlled profile where caution must be exercised to avoid backdraft.

## For firefighters: what do air factors tell us?

- The presence of air inlets can indicate whether a fire has a fuel-controlled or ventilation-controlled profile.
- No visible air inlets may suggest a ventilation-controlled situation, but should be assessed alongside the available air that is already within a building, open plan layouts etc.
- Multiple air inlets can cause turbulence of fire gases and rapid fire developments.
- If we can identify a single opening acting as an air inlet and smoke outlet (bi-directional flowpath) we may be able to use this as an exhaust vent if we create another inlet opening and attack via that route.

- If a unidirectional flowpath is already created (one air inlet, one smoke/fire gas outlet) we can use this to our advantage and increase the speed of attack.
- The 'kill zone', or outlet side of the flowpath, can be identified and crews briefed and tactics made accordingly.
- 'Sucking' of air at inlets can be signs of vent controlled profiles, creating negative pressures and backdraft potential.
- 'Belching' can suggest a 'sealed', wind-driven fire and tactics can be altered to avoid 'blowtorch' effects, as covered in Volume 1.

## Aide memoire: Air factors

| Indicator | Flashover | Backdraft | Fire Gas Ignition |
|---|---|---|---|
| Flow path | Smooth bidirectional air tracks indicate fuel-controlled conditions. Turbulence at the neutral plane indicates a ventilation controlled profile. Combined with lowering neutral plane. | Less apparent due to limited number or size of openings. Look for openings alternating between unidirectional inlet to a unidirectional outlet on initial opening. Smoke is often turbulent and expanding. | The further the smoke moves from the compartment of origin, the more likely the interface will be smooth and appear benign. |
| Pulsations | Not seen in the fuel-controlled phase, but may present to some extent in the ventilation controlled phase. | Often present. Rapid pulsations usually mean higher temperatures. | Highly unlikely. |
| Whistling sounds | Unlikely. | Pulsing air forced in and out of small gaps may make this sound. | Highly unlikely. |

# Chapter 7:
# Reading fire step 5 – heat factors

Heat signatures can often be tricky to spot and it is here where recent(ish) technology has become our friend. Thermal image cameras can greatly assist us during an initial size up to identify clues that heat presents. And, lucky you, we will be covering the tactical use of thermal image cameras in Volume 3.

All items have a 'thermal capacity'. An object will absorb heat and act as a 'passive' agent until it reaches this thermal limit, or capacity, and begins to contribute that heat back into a compartment. Items such as bricks have high thermal capacities and this heat can be identified by thermal imaging. We can use this to our advantage during size up.

Some of the heat factors we need to consider will correspond to other factors in the assessment process, for example blackened windows, which also can indicate a low neutral plane, suggest that we have a ventilation controlled profile where gases are above their flammable range and 'too rich' to burn. Windows can also become distorted by heat, and surrounding fixtures, particularly those consisting of polymers or plastics, can melt or warp, giving another indicator of particularly intense heat presence.

Glass is also susceptible to 'thermal shock'. It's important to look out for cracks in the glass caused by a sudden build up in heat. Furthermore, sudden reductions in heat can causes cracks or failures so we should exercise caution when applying water to avoid making unwanted openings and creating more flowpaths. Glasswork can show more of a 'crazing' effect (fine cracks) where the heat buildup has been slower and steadier. And in some situations, where the heat has had to travel some distance throughout the building, there may be no evidence of this at all. Each of these can be a signal indicating a potential for backdraft, flashover or fire gas ignition.

Figure 7.1 shows severely blackened windows (heat) with an extremely low neutral plane (smoke) that almost touches the ground. These are both indicators of a ventilation controlled fire profile with 'rich' fire gases above their flammable range wanting to mix with air and dilute down into the range so they can burn.

## Figure 7.1: The effects of heat and smoke on windows

Grimwood *et al* (2005) note that a sudden heat build up internally is an indication that gaseous phase combustion has commenced in the ceiling area. It is agreed that, as an indicator, this could well be too late. Actions can be taken before we get to this stage such as 'temperature checks' by water application into smoke layers, which we shall cover in Volume 3.

Blistered paintwork can also be an indicator of heat build up. Painted surfaces on lightly insulated doors and walls (with lower thermal capacity) can begin to bubble and blister. It is perhaps likely that a change in colour of paintwork that is exposed to heat will be more visible to the naked eye (see Figure 7.2).

## Figure 7.2: Heat damaged paintwork

Heated surfaces can present a number of clues that we can decipher, but we shouldn't be too hasty into making assumptions. A compartment's surface may not show signs of heat, but could contain fire gases within their flammable range, waiting for an ignition source (fire gas ignition). As we know, as all available oxygen is used up within ventilation controlled fires, burning can cease, heat release can reduce and temperatures can fall, so situations with the potential for backdraft may not always show signs of heat.

### For firefighters, what do the heat factors mean to us?

- First and very importantly, we should be looking for areas of heat using a thermal image camera wherever possible.
- Severe heat in one area can indicate proximity to fire, however as the heat travels through cooler air, indicators may be less obvious, but the risk of fire gas ignition, with fire gases diluted into their flammable range even though they're at lower temperatures, is increased.
- Severe blackening of windows indicate where hot fire gases are 'too rich' to burn, meaning the concentration and flammability limits are crucial and air tactics should be relevant and appropriate.
- Heat signatures will give an indication of fire location, particularly if the fire profile is fuel controlled.
- Bricks and other materials with higher thermal capacities will absorb and retain heat, but may take longer to warm up than lightweight materials that soon reach their capacity and become 'active' and 'emitters'.

## Aide memoire: Heat factors

| Indicator | Flashover | Backdraft | Fire gas ignition |
|---|---|---|---|
| **Paintwork blistered or discoloured** (Heat indicators may be less obvious in structures with heavy insulation.) | Often present on outside of lightly constructed/insulated doors or walls. Can give a relative indicator of the location of the fire compartment. | Discoloration may give indication of heat layering. A light application of water in the external surface will evaporate at temperatures over 100°C (212°F) providing a visible heat indicator in lightweight construction. | A lack of heat indicators could be deceptive. The further the smoke has travelled the greater the cooling effect. Pre-mixing of the unburnt fuel with air may form a mixture within flammable limits. Mixture close to ideal may be explosive! |
| **Windows** Soot stained Condensate Cracking/crazing | Darkening will most likely be present. Windows may crack if the heat build-up is sudden (or if jets are applied to super-heated glass). | Darkening indicates rich conditions. Cracking indicates high heat conditions. Crazing may indicate a more gradual temperature increase has occurred. | Darkening may be present as the smoke accumulates. Cracking is less likely in the early stages especially if the smoke has cooled by travelling an extended distance. |
| **Hot surfaces** (May be absent in structures with heavy insulation.) | Often present in lightweight construction. | Surfaces may be hot & the temperature will gradually decrease as the available oxygen is consumed. | May not be hot, particularly in the early stages. |

| Indicator | Flashover | Backdraft | Fire gas ignition |
|---|---|---|---|
| Sudden increase in interior temperature | A very late indicator and therefore of no use in giving early warning! Gas cool and/or remove the smoke. | A very late indicator and therefore of no use in giving early warning. Anti-ventilate and/or cool smoke before ventilation & have charged hose line in place! | None until the fire gas ignition. Fire gas ignition can be very sudden and even explosive. The explosive power depends on the amount of fuel and how well it has pre-mixed with the available air. |

# Chapter 8: Reading fire step 6 – flame factors

There is a tendency for firefighters to focus on any visible flame on arrival at a scene. There is nothing inherently wrong with this as long as it does not lead to a loss of situational awareness. However, unless the structure is totally involved, it is still critical to read all of the fire behaviour indicators to get a complete picture of the current stage of fire development, and the likely path of fire extension.

At the end of the day flames are the 'end product' of combustion, showing us that we have something on fire and it is right that they demand our full attention and understanding. However, we need to distinguish between types of combustion to help us a little here.

Smoke is a fuel, and when the fire gases that smoke consists of are burning it is known as 'gaseous phase combustion'. Now, as we all know, smoke (fire gas) can travel significant distances, so if we are in a gaseous phase combustion situation, the flames we observe may be some distance from the actual materials that are on fire – the 'fuel bed' or 'fuel package'. If we know where the fuel bed is and the origin of the fire, we can use appropriate tactics and reduce gas phase combustion by direct application onto the burning materials. The fuel bed and point of fire origin is what we should be trying to identify during our size up.

We should remember that 'remote ignitions' are a form of gaseous phase combustion. These are where we see visible flames seemingly 'disconnected' from a body of smoke after leaving a compartment in a form that is 'too rich' to burn, and then mixing with air and diluting down into the flammable range and auto-igniting. This also links back with heat and smoke factors indicating a ventilation controlled profile with potential for backdraft.

Any flames appearing around the interface/ neutral plane once an opening has been created is a very late and dangerous sign that rich gases are diluting into their flammable range in temperatures that can auto ignite them (see Figure 8.1)

## Figure 8.1: Auto ignition

Note the visible flame as air from the created opening dilutes smoke/ fire gas into its flammable range and the high heat causes 'auto ignition'.

The colour of flames is another indicator that can be used to assess the situation and the burning profile effectively.

There is a crude rule of thumb that says a flame burns brightest when it is hottest, but we must remember that the availability of air, the type of fuel and pyrolysis products generated can all influence this.

It is perhaps with regard to the influence of air that we can begin to analyse flame colours.

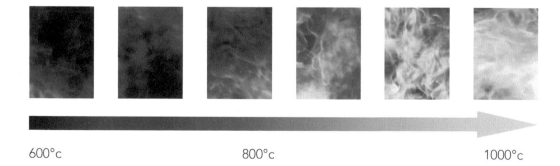

600°c                                    800°c                                    1000°c

(Lambert & Baaij, 2015. Reprinted with kind permission of the authors.)

If a flame has a reduced air supply, there is a tendency of flames to burn a deeper red or orange colour. This can indicate that there is less available oxygen and the gases are burning at the richer end of their flammable range. These flames will appear to be more turbulent and 'choppy' in form as they search for additional oxygen. Given that this is the case, and air supply is a critical factor, these should inform our tactics. At the other end of the spectrum, a plentiful air supply will generate a whiter or yellower flame. As we know, sufficient air supply can lead us towards flashover and along the usual fire development curve.

It has also been stated that pyrolysis products and accumulated carbon monoxide that has diluted into its flammable range can result in blue flames around the neutral plane.

Paul Grimwood identified this back in 1999 on the website www.firetactics.com in an article 'Flashover & nozzle techniques', later cited in *3D Firefighting*, and he attributes these blue flames to 'incomplete combustion and the presence of a high percentage of pyrolysis products' (Grimwood *et al*, 2005).

Let us also remember that we can see a variation of colours in one compartment. Yellow flames at a lower level in the fuel bed can be significantly lighter than those higher up in the compartment where they are surrounded by pyrolysis products and oxygen concentration is significantly less.

If we can't see any flames at all we must rely on other factors, but we should be aware of the potential for fire gas ignitions and backdrafts before making entry and creating ventilation points.

The colour of a flame can provide valuable clues as to whether a fire has sufficient air supply or not, and how our tactics should take advantage of this to maximise the impact of our operations. Once crews are committed within a structure, any flames in the smoke layer or gaseous combustion should be regarded as a critical warning that immediate action is required. This is an extremely dangerous situation.

## For firefighters, what are the flames saying to me?

- Flame colour can indicate the fire profile (fuel or ventilation controlled).
- A whiter flame can indicate hotter temperatures and a richer supply of oxygen.
- Remote Ignitions and flaming can show fire gases are above their auto-ignition temperatures but 'too rich to burn', influencing our tactical selection.
- Flames in the smoke/fire gas layer are an indication of impending flashover.
- Fire spread means visible flames may actually be some distance from the 'fuel package' or room of origin.
- Lack of visible flames in conjunction with previous BE-SAHF factors can indicate potential for rapid fire developments.

## Aide memoire: Flame factors

| Indicator | Flashover | Backdraft | Fire gas ignition |
|---|---|---|---|
| Location & volume | Caution! Visible flame may have spread some distance from the initial seat of fire. Look for the seat and/or multiple points of origin. | Little or no visible flame, but conditions can vary widely in different parts of the structure. Super-heated fuel rich smoke may auto ignite after leaving the compartment of origin. | No flame in adjacent areas prior to FGI. After ignition it is likely to be progress very rapidly (or explosively). Cool the gases and/or remove accumulated smoke! |
| Auto-ignition: Remote ignition outside of an opening. | Indicates that the internal conditions are very hot (above auto-ignition temperature) and too rich to support full flaming combustion inside the compartment. | May be seen occurring as pulsed smoke is pushed out. May aslo occur after opening up the compartment. Can trigger backdraft | Less likely to trigger FGI than an ember or flame extension. |

| Indicator | Flashover | Backdraft | Fire gas ignition |
|---|---|---|---|
| Flames forming in the smoke layer | Isolated flames traveling in the hot gas layer. May not be visible without a TIC. Indicates impending rollover and flashover. | Could occur after ventilation if water is not introduced. | Not likely. |
| Roll over<br><br>Ignited fire gases roll across the ceiling leading to a massive increase in heat. | This is a late indicator of flashover and it not always visible to the naked eye. Use your TIC and prevent it with gas cooling. | May occur after ventilation if the backdraft is not triggered early by auto-ignition or embers. | Roll over in the compartment of origin could progress into the smoke accumulated in adjacent areas and trigger FGI. |
| Colour<br><br>Can be influenced by many variables | Yellow colouring at the base of the fire often indicates good air flow. Reddish orange flames may indicate less air is available or the conditions are fuel rich. | Red or orange may indicate fuel rich conditions. Pockets of blue flames are said to be from the auto-ignition of carbon monoxide. | No flame may be present in the space prior to ignition. |

# Chapter 9:
# Be safe, not too late
# – a small case study

We're now going to take a brief look at an incident in a BE-SAHF context. Let's review what signs we can identify in the images below for each of the areas we've looked at, and consider, not criticise, whether we would make different decisions here.

The following situation demonstrates what can happen if we don't pay proper attention to the BE-SAHF principles or the indicators of rapid fire developments such as backdraft.

This chapter consists of a series of images taken in quick succession as a pair of firefighters attempt to gain access to a burning building. Each image is followed by a table highlighting the important points that can be observed and that should be taken into account in similar situations.

So, let's get started!

## Step 1
### Figure 9.1

| Building<br>Flashover<br>Backdraft<br>FGI | 1. We have a large area of single pane glass. Expect rapid fire growth if windows fail.<br>2. If this is a shop there is a potential for high fire loading and for oxygen to be used up quickly, heightening the risk of backdraft.<br>3. There will potentially be voids allowing fire gases to accumulate, which raises the risk of FGI.<br>4. Consider whether there is a basement and if the fire could be located there. It is possible that, due to lack of ventilation, it is creating lots of pyrolysis products or heating the floor above causing FGI potential on the ground floor. |
|---|---|
| Environment<br>Air direction and velocity | No noticeable signs of wind impact. |
| Smoke<br>Volume/location<br>Colour<br>Buoyancy<br>Height of neutral plane | 1. There is little smoke visible at this time from this perspective.<br>2. The dark colour indicates ventilation limited combustion. So ventilation (adding air) will most likely intensify the fire. |
| Air<br>Bidirectional<br>Unidirectional<br>Pulsations/alternating flow path | The opening created with the axe appears to be creating a unidirectional inlet. |
| Heat<br>Blistering or discoloration of paintwork<br>Cracking or crazing of windows<br>Condensate, tar or soot on windows<br>Hot surfaces<br>Sudden increase in temperature | Blackened windows, heat distortion/cracks – could be a sign of backdraft conditions. |

| Flame | None visible from this angle at this time. |
|---|---|
| Location and volume | |
| Auto-ignition | |
| Pocketing in smoke layer | |
| Rollover | |
| Colour (red to orange to yellow) | |

# Step 2
## Figure 9.2

| Building | No change or additional information |
|---|---|
| Flashover | |
| Backdraft | |
| FGI | |
| Environment | No change or additional information. |
| Air direction and velocity | |

| | |
|---|---|
| **Smoke**<br><br>Volume/location<br><br>Colour<br><br>Buoyancy<br><br>Height of neutral plane | 1. Smoke emerging low and as a unidirectional exhaust.<br>2. Smoke is a dark colour indicating ventilation limited combustion.<br>3. Buoyant and expanding low neutral plane. |
| **Air**<br><br>Bidirectional<br><br>Unidirectional<br><br>Pulsations/alternating flow path | Change to unidirectional exhaust is a classic backdraft warning sign. |
| **Heat**<br><br>Blistering or discoloration of paintwork<br><br>Cracking or crazing of windows<br><br>Condensate, tar or soot on windows<br><br>Hot surfaces<br><br>Sudden increase in temperature | Blackened windows, heat distortion/cracks – (Backdraft?) |
| **Flame**<br><br>Location and volume<br><br>Auto-ignition<br><br>Pocketing in smoke layer<br><br>Rollover<br><br>Colour (red to orange to yellow) | None visible from this angle at this time. |

# Step 3
## Figure 9.3

| Building<br>Flashover<br>Backdraft<br>FGI | No change or additional information |
|---|---|
| **Environment**<br>Air direction and velocity | No change or additional information. |
| **Smoke**<br>Volume/location<br>Colour<br>Buoyancy<br>Height of neutral plane | 1. Volume and velocity increasing rapidly.<br>2. Dark colour of smoke suggests rich combustion.<br>3. Buoyant and expanding fire gases.<br>4. Very low neutral plane. |
| **Air**<br>Bidirectional<br>Unidirectional<br>Pulsations/alternating flow path | Unidirectional exhaust is increasing in velocity and volume – backdraft warning sign. |

| Heat | Blackening rapidly increasing. |
| --- | --- |
| Blistering or discoloration of paintwork | |
| Cracking or crazing of windows | |
| Condensate, tar, or soot on windows | |
| Hot surfaces | |
| Sudden increase in temperature | |
| **Flame** | None visible from this angle at this time. |
| Location and volume | |
| Auto-ignition | |
| Pocketing in smoke layer | |
| Rollover | |
| Colour (red to orange to yellow) | |

# Step 4

## Figure 9.4

| Building<br>Flashover<br>Backdraft<br>FGI | No change or additional information |
|---|---|
| Environment<br>Air direction and velocity | No change or additional information. |
| Smoke<br>Volume/location<br>Colour<br>Buoyancy<br>Height of neutral plane | 1. Volume and velocity increasing rapidly.<br>2. Buoyant and expanding fire gases.<br>3. Very low neutral plane. |
| Air<br>Bidirectional<br>Unidirectional<br>Pulsations/alternating flow path | Unidirectional exhaust is increasing in velocity and volume – backdraft has commenced! |
| Heat<br>Blistering or discoloration of paintwork<br>Cracking or crazing of windows<br>Condensate, tar or soot on windows<br>Hot surfaces<br>Sudden increase in temperature | Blackening rapidly increasing. |
| Flame<br>Location and volume<br>Auto-ignition<br>Pocketing in smoke layer<br>Rollover<br>Colour (red to orange to yellow) | The transformation of smoke to flame (red to orange) has commenced just inside the doorway. |

# Step 5
## Figure 9.5

| Building<br>Flashover<br>Backdraft<br>FGI | No change or additional information |
|---|---|
| **Environment**<br>Air direction and velocity | No change or additional information. |
| **Smoke**<br>Volume/location<br>Colour<br>Buoyancy<br>Height of neutral plane | 1. Volume and velocity still increasing.<br>2. Lighter colour indicates improved combustion efficiency.<br>3. Buoyant and expanding (hot).<br>4. Very low neutral plane. |
| **Air**<br>Bidirectional<br>Unidirectional<br>Pulsations/alternating flow path | 1. Unidirectional exhaust of smoke transitions to flame.<br>2. Backdraft progresses outside of the opening. |

| Heat | 1. Transition from hot smoke to flame. |
|---|---|
| Blistering or discoloration of paintwork | 2. Temperature rapidly increasing. |
| Cracking or crazing of windows | |
| Condensate, tar or soot on windows | |
| Hot surfaces | |
| Sudden increase in temperature | |
| **Flame** | 1. Yellow to orange flame commencing at the base of opening where there is the best air supply. |
| Location and volume | 2. Triggered by auto-ignition as it comes into contact with the air outside the building. |
| Auto-ignition | |
| Pocketing in smoke layer | |
| Rollover | |
| Colour (red to orange to yellow) | |

# Step 6

## Figure 9.6

| Building<br><br>Flashover<br><br>Backdraft<br><br>FGI | No change or additional information. |
|---|---|
| Environment<br><br>Air direction and velocity | No change or additional information. |
| Smoke<br><br>Volume/location<br><br>Colour<br><br>Buoyancy<br><br>Height of neutral plane | 1. Volume and velocity increasing rapidly.<br>2. Buoyant and expanding.<br>3. Very low neutral plane. |
| Air<br><br>Bidirectional<br><br>Unidirectional<br><br>Pulsations/alternating flow path | 1. A total unidirectional exhaust approaching peak intensity.<br>2. Well-developed backdraft. |
| Heat<br><br>Blistering or discoloration of paintwork<br><br>Cracking or crazing of windows<br><br>Condensate, tar or soot on windows<br><br>Hot surfaces<br><br>Sudden increase in temperature | Transition from hot smoke to flame increasing. |
| Flame<br><br>Location and volume<br><br>Auto-ignition<br><br>Pocketing in smoke layer<br><br>Rollover<br><br>Colour (red to orange to yellow) | 1. Yellow to orange flame progressing.<br>2. White flame indicates very high temperatures in lower part of the opening. |

# The analysis

So how do the actions in the photographs relate to the stages of fire development? In short, if we revisit Volume 1 and have a look at Figure 9.7 below, we can see that the crucial factor is the point of increased ventilation. In this case, caused by the breaking of the windows in step 1.

## Figure 9.7: Vent induced flashover

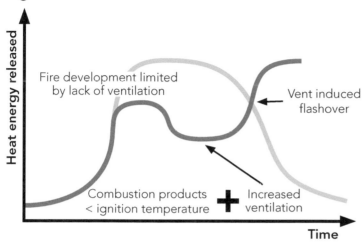

(CFBT US- Ed Hartin)

## Figure 9.8: Backdraft

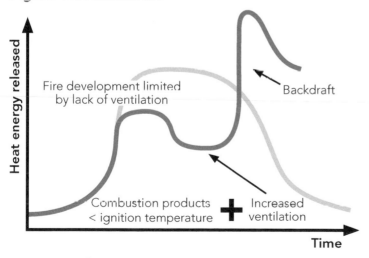

(CFBT US- Ed Hartin)

## For firefighters, what do these photos and graphics this show us?

It is absolutely critical that the BE-SAHF assessment takes place as an overall and related assessment. The timing of making the assessment is crucial and must take place before any tactical operations take place.

The photos used above were taken in a time frame of less than 15 seconds, so we can see how rapidly things can change.

Some questions to consider:

Would you use the same tactics as the crew?

If not, what tactics would you use instead?

Don't worry to too much if you can't answer the second question yet. Volume 3 in this series will give you a number of options, tactics and techniques to bring into play.

# Chapter 10:
# Your turn at reading fire

So, having covered the basics of making a BE-SAHF assessment, it's over to you to undertake an assessment of each of the following images using the knowledge you've picked up. There's nobody watching, so feel free to refer back to previous chapters and your notes here.

We would suggest printing out one copy of the BE-SAHF assessment form at the end of the chapter for each of the images and complete it to the best of your ability.

## Image 1

(GettyImages, Stephen St. John)

## Image 2

(GettyImages, Gabe Palmer)

## Image 3

(GettyImages)

# BE-SAHF assessment sheet

| Indicator | On arrival |
|---|---|
| **Building**<br>Flashover<br>Backdraft<br>FGI | |
| **Environment**<br>Air direction and velocity | |
| **Smoke**<br>Volume/location<br>Colour<br>Buoyancy<br>Height of neutral plane | |
| **Air**<br>Bidirectional<br>Unidirectional<br>Pulsations/alternating flow path | |
| **Heat**<br>Blistering or discoloration of paintwork<br>Cracking or crazing of windows<br>Condensate, tar or soot on windows<br>Hot surfaces<br>Sudden increase in temperature | |
| **Flame**<br>Location and volume<br>Auto-ignition<br>Pocketing in smoke layer<br>Rollover<br>Colour (red to orange to yellow) | |

# Chapter 11: Reading the fire – a summary

Well, we've almost made it to the end of this volume. Before we sign off though, and move onto *Volume 3: Fighting Fire*, let's have a quick reminder of how the BE-SAHF factors give us indicators of the stage of a fire's development and its profile.

Reading the fire is like learning a language. Every fire is 'speaking' to us through its behaviour indicators. Sometimes the fire is talking softly and even if we understand the language we must be paying close attention or we will miss the message. Sometimes the indicators are so clear that the fire is shouting at us, but if we don't understand the language, then it doesn't matter how loud or clear the message is. Sometimes the fire tells lies. It deceives us by only telling part of the story, by concealing critical information. So not only must we know the language of fire, we must also be aware that it will not always tell us everything unless we keep seeking input and reading between the lines.

Firefighters regularly work in dangerous and rapidly changing environments. They must make decisions in seconds with very limited information, and take actions that may save or endanger lives. The best we can do is to base those decisions on our knowledge of building construction and visible fire behaviour indicators at each stage of the incident. There are no easy answers, but as scientific research enlightens our knowledge of fire behaviour, we must be prepared to challenge our traditional thinking and be prepared to open our minds to new possibilities.

Key points in reading the fire:

- Determine the fire's location.

- Determine the stage of development using smoke and air indicators.

- The air indicators help to establish the openings that are feeding the fire with essential air, and the exhaust paths, which will tell us which way the fire is heading.

- When there are few smoke and air indicators, the heat indicators can assist in determining the likely fire base.

- Flame indicators can assist in establishing the likely fire seat and the direction of fire spread.

- Never rely on one indicator! Read them all in the context of the building factors and ambient environmental factors.

- All firefighters should be observing the FBI in their area of operation and should relay this critical information to the incident commander and update this whenever there are any noticeable changes.

- The process is dynamic and must continue until the fireground is vacated.

In the next book, we will cover how the stage of the fire will influence our tactics and our ability to dominate the fire by manipulating the two sides of the fire triangle that we can readily influence – heat and oxygen (air). Reading the fire with BE-SAHF can lead to the development of the most effective fire attack plan by using a variety of tactics, tools and techniques. The correct combination will enable us to take control of the fire efficiently and safely.

But, keeping it simple… What we want to avoid is making an uncontrolled entry and contributing to a rapid fire development by admission of air (either a backdraft or ventilation induced flashover), or allowing flaming combustion to reach accumulated fuels (FGI). Cool the surrounding surface and if possible introduce water into the smoke filled compartment BEFORE ventilation.

Treat all smoke as potentially ignitable. Isolate it, cool it and/or remove it.

We want to avoid a situation such as that depicted in Figure 11.1 in which a fire that has become ventilation controlled suddenly gets a rich new source of oxygen allowing it to rapidly develop.

## Figure 11.1: How not to do it – feeding a ventilation-controlled fire

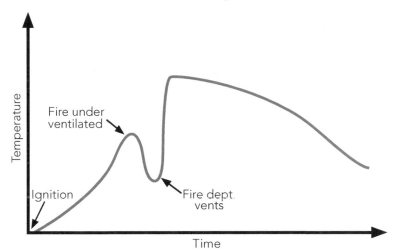

(Adapted with permission of UL/NIST.)

Look at Figure 11.2 below and then compare each stage of fire development, from incipient to decay, with the chart in Figure 11.3 that follows.

## Figure 11.2: Fuel-controlled fire development

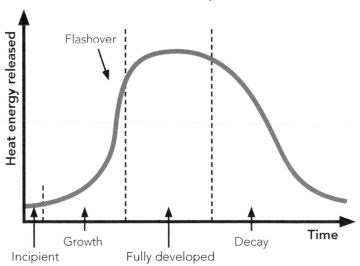

The chart in Figure 11.3 explores each stage of development of a fuel-controlled fire and gives examples of how the BE-SAHF principles might apply at each stage, or what needs to be considered. Along the top of the chart is the stage of fire you might encounter, and the column will give all the important considerations for each component of the BE-SAHF model.

## Figure 11.3: BE-SAHF indicators of a fuel-controlled fire

| | | Incipient | Growth | Flashover | Fully developed | Decay |
|---|---|---|---|---|---|---|
| B | | Compartment size Fuel geometry Fixed installations | | | | |
| E | | | Wind/ moisture can begin to impact here causing the fire to develop quickly. | | | |
| S | | Limited smoke, no defined neutral plane. Light colour, limited buoyancy. | Smoke layer visible, movement of smoke. PVT principles. | Rapid lowering of neutral plane, fire gases may become darker. | May darken with increased volume & density. Neutral plane level affected by available ventilation. | Heat release rate reduces, but increased temperature can release pyrolysis products/ fuel rich gases. |

|   | Incipient | Growth | Flashover | Fully developed | Decay |
|---|-----------|--------|-----------|-----------------|-------|
| A | Thermal Image Camera (TIC) may observe some inward air movement near the fire location. | Bi or uni-directional flowpaths may be visible. Speed of air intake & smoke discharge increases. | Increased air movement & velocity of flowpaths (inlet & outlet). | Well defined & strong air motion on 'inlet flowpath'. | |
| H | Temperatures circa ambient. Some water vapour pyrolysis may be seen as condensation on windows. | Windows begin to stain, possibly crack at upper levels. TIC may now pick up heat signatures from external positions. | Pyrolysis observed some distance from fire origin can indicate flashover. | Visual indicators can include black windows, crazed glass, hot surfaces. | |
| F | Small flames, restricted to a small area. | Flames at ceiling level, some gaseous combustion may be visible from outside. | Flames in the gas layer – rollover. | Flames visible – whole compartment involved. | |

Figure 11.4 shows a fire development curve where the supply of oxygen to a fire is limited, thus giving a ventilation controlled profile. If we compare this to previous scenario (Figure 11.2), we can see that the BE-SAHF factors that present are significantly different.

Let's revise a limited or ventilation controlled profile and fire development, then look at the BE-SAHF factors that MAY present (Figure 11.5).

## Figure 11.4: Fire development with limited ventilation

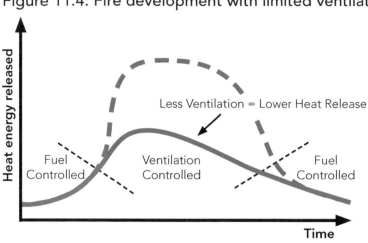

So let's repeat the process and look at the BE-SAHF factors that present during the period that the fire has become ventilation controlled, you may remember from Volume 1 that some refer to this as a 'false decay'.

## Figure 11.5: BE-SAHF indicators of a ventilation-controlled fire

| | 'False decay' period – 'ventilation controlled' |
|---|---|
| B | Restricted compartment size or available air supply has caused available air to be used up and flaming combustion to diminish or cease. Heavily insulated buildings, double/triple glazing can be warning signals. |
| E | Environmental factors are usually not a factor here, except in very cold temperatures with increased oxygen content causing even more rapid escalation if unconsidered ventilation made. |
| S | Low or 'bouncing' smoke layer, fire gases pulsing or exiting under pressure from gaps, potentially with remote ignition when mixing with air externally. Optically dense smoke, darkening as soot is produced from incomplete combustion. |
| A | Air may be 'pulsing' in and high pressure, turbulent fire gases discharged. This is affected by inlet size and proximity to fire. Inrush of air/'whistling sounds' may be seen/heard. |
| H | Temperatures can continue to increase initially, blackening windows and heat can cause further release of pyrolysis gases. |
| F | Turbulent, 'choppy' flames, may be red/deep orange. Remote ignitions may be observed externally in escaping gases, there will be a reduction in flaming combustion. |

# Moving on...

So, there we are. Another Volume down and we're ready to move on to *Volume 3: Fighting Fire*. This book has aimed to give you a good understanding of the main factors that need to be understood in order to properly 'read' a fire and size up a situation upon arrival. It is not intended to be entirely comprehensive and there will be much more for you to learn on the ground. But we hope this will have given you a solid foundation of knowledge upon which to build.

As with so much, it is practise that will make perfect.

The next volume, *Fighting Fire*, takes what we have learned in this book and *Volume 1: Fire Dynamics for Firefighters* and provides you with the information you'll need to make tactical decisions based on your knowledge of fire and your BE-SAHF assessment. It will explore many of the techniques that are available to us, when they might be used and how they can be deployed most effectively.

It covers the use of thermal imaging cameras, air ventilation including PPV and hydraulic ventilation, as well as techniques for controlling smoke using smoke curtains and door control. It then moves on to discuss a range of water application techniques, from the basic principles and tactical flow rates to gas cooling tactics and nozzle techniques including straight streaming, pencilling, steam suppression and combined attacks. It looks at high pressure systems, CAFS, foam and other agents, as well as movement principles including door entry and positions of optimal outcome. Finally, the book offers some practical information about determining what tactics could be chosen and a checklist to guide decision making, as well as introducing the STAR model of decision making and how the information in this series can be combined with other models and approaches from around the world.

We hope you enjoyed the book, and we hope you'll find the next volume equally as informative and engaging.

# References and further reading

## Books

Baaij S & Lambert K (2015) *Fire Dynamics: Technical approach, tactical application*. SDU, Netherlands.

Bengtsson, Lars-Göran (2001) *Enclosure Fires*. NRS Tryckeri: Huskvarna.

Braidwood J (1866) *Fire Prevention & Fire Extinction*. London: Bell & Daldy.

Brunacini A (1985) *Fire Command* (2nd Edition). Boston: National Fire Protection Association.

Brunacini N (2012) *Staring into the Sun*. Phoenix, AZ: Nick Brunacini Publications.

DeHaan JD & Icove D (2002) *Kirk's Fire Investigation* (5th Edition). New Jersey: Prentice Hall.

Drysdale D (2011) *An Introduction to Fire Dynamics* (3rd Edition). Edinburgh: Willey.

Gorbett GE & Pharr JL (2010) *Fire Dynamics*. New Jersey: Prentice Hall.

Grimwood P (2008) *Euro Firefighter*. Huddersfield: Jeremy Mills Publishing.

Grimwood P, Hartin E, McDonough J & Raffel S (2005) *3D Firefighting*. United States: University of Oregon press.

Institution of Fire Engineers (2004). *Elementary Fire Engineering Handbook* (3rd Edition). Leicester: IFE publications.

Karlsson B & Quintiere JG (1999) *Enclosure Fire Dynamics*. Florida: CRC Press.

Layman L (1955) *Firefighting Tactics*. Boston: National Fire Protection Association.

Layman L (1940) *Fundamentals of Firefighting Tactics*. California: Macgruder Publishing.

Särdqvist S (2002) *Water and other Extinguishing Agents*. NRS Trickeri: Huskvarna.

Svensson S (2005) *Fire Ventilation*. NRS Trickeri: Huskvarna.

Taylor J (2007) *Smoke Burns*. UK: Quack Books.

## Manuals

Home Office (1997) *Fire Service Manual Volume 2: Compartment fires & tactical ventilation*. London: The Stationary Office.

Home Office (1998) *Fire Service Manual Volume 1: Physics & chemistry for firefighters*. London: The Stationary Office.

Home Office (2001) *Fire Service Manual Volume 3: Basic principles of building & construction*. London: The Stationary Office.

## Websites

Fishlock M (2012) *High Rise Firefighting co uk* [online]. Available at: http://www.highrisefirefighting.co.uk (accessed June 2017).

Hartin E (2010) *Compartment Fire Behaviour Training – United States* [online]. Available at: http://www.cfbt-us.com (accessed June 2017).

Raffel S (2017) *Safe Zone of Buffer Zone?* [online]. Available at: http://www.3dfirefighting.com/images/Downloads/SafeZone_or_Buffer_Zone.pdf (accessed June 2017).

Raffel S (2015) *Fire Gas Ignition – The Hidden Killer* [online]. Available at: http://www.3dfirefighting. com/images/Fire_Gas_Ignition3.pdf (accessed June 2017).

Raffel S (2011) *The Art of "Reading Fire"* [online]. Available at: http://www.firefighternation.com/ articles/2011/07/the-art-of-reading-fire.html (accessed June 2017).

Raffel S (2013) *New Developments in Reading Fire: Strategy and tactics* [online]. Available at: http:// www.firerescuemagazine.com/articles/print/volume-8/issue-12/strategy-and-tactics/new-developments- in-reading-fire.html (accessed June 2017).

NIST (2017) *Recent News* [online]. United States Department of Commerce: National Institute of Standards & Technology. Available at: http://www.nist.gov/fire/ (accessed June 2017).

## Journals

Boj-Garcia P (2016) Offensive Fire Attack: Variables that interfere with the fire gases outlet: Part 1 [online]. *International Fire Fighter Magazine*. Available at: http://iffmag.mdmpublishing.com/offensive- fire-attack-variables-that-interfere-with-the-fire-gases-outlet-part-1/ (accessed June 2017).

Grimwood P (2000) Compartment Firefighting: Finding the right flow rates. *FIRE magazine*. 1 September. Brighton: Pavilion Publishing.

Raffel S (2013) Explaining the unexpected. *FireRescue Magazine*, December 2013.

Raffel S (2014) Learn & BE SAHF. *Fire & Rescue Magazine*, 1st Quarter, p 14–17.

Raffel S (2014) Understanding fires. *Fire & Rescue Magazine*, 3rd Quarter 2014, p 20.

## University theses

Dave J (2012) *Heat Release Rate: The single most important variable in fire*. MSc Fire Dynamics dissertation, University of Leeds, United Kingdom.

BV - #0084 - 200622 - C14 - 246/185/7 - PB - 9781911028734 - Gloss Lamination